With editorial collaboration and a special chapter
on selection, care, and training of your dog, by
LAURENCE ALDEN HORSWELL
Judge and technical canine authority

DOGS
OF THE WORLD

BY PATRICK LAWSON
ILLUSTRATED BY SHANNON STIRNWEIS

Golden Press New York

Western Publishing Company, Inc.

CONTENTS

the first dogs
page 10

Hyena; Dhole; Antarctic Wolf; Simian Fox; Andean Wolf; Red or Maned Wolf; Dingo

sporting dogs
page 18

SPANIELS: American Cocker (solid color, black; ascob; parti-color); English Cocker; Clumber; Sussex; Field; English Springer; Welsh Springer; Brittany; Irish Water; American Water; SETTERS: Irish; English; Gordon; POINTERS: Weimaraner; German Shorthaired; German Wirehaired; Wirehaired Pointing Griffon; Vizsla (Hungarian Pointer); RETRIEVERS: Curly-Coated; Flat-Coated; Golden; Chesapeake Bay; Labrador

hounds
page 28

Basenji; Rhodesian Ridgeback; Greyhound; Whippet; Saluki; Afghan; Borzoi; Norwegian Elkhound; Scottish Deerhound; Irish Wolfhound; Beagle; Agassaeus; Otterhound; Southern Hound; Welsh Harrier; Basset Hound; Bloodhound; English Foxhound; American Foxhound; Harrier; Dachshund—Longhaired, Wirehaired, Miniature; Black and Tan Coonhound; Talbot Hound; Virginia Foxhound

working dogs
page 42

Collie—Rough, Smooth, Border; Bernese Mountain Dog; Old English Sheepdog; Welsh Corgi—Pembroke Corgi, Cardigan Corgi; Briard; Bouvier des Flandres; Belgian Sheepdog; Belgian Tervuren; Belgian Malinois; German Shepherd; Great Pyrenees; Mastiff; Bull Mastiff; St. Bernard, Swiss Alpine St. Bernard; Puli; Kuvasz; Komondor; Great Dane; Boxer; Rottweiler; Doberman Pinscher; German Pinscher; Standard Schnauzer; Giant Schnauzer; Newfoundland; Siberian Husky (Siberian Chuchi); Alaskan Malamute; Eskimo Dog; Samoyed; Akita; Australian Cattle Dog; Australian Kelpie

CONTENTS

HYENA

the first dogs

THE DOG has been called man's best friend. This is not a description of idle companionship. From the earliest records of man's struggle for survival, the dog has been his active partner. He has helped hunt down the savage, wild boar, the swift-footed deer, the birds of the air in order that man and his family might eat. He has aided in killing man's enemies such as the wolf, the bear, the fox, the rat, and the badger.

He has been man's vigilant sentry, his guard. He has rescued him from fire, flood, the desert's heat, and the snow's bitter cold. Time without end, he has willingly given up his life to save man and that which belonged to man.

As civilization gradually replaced savagery, the friend-

ship of dog for man has been tested in countless ways. In the Middle Ages, protected by a brass-studded collar or clad in a coat of armor, the dog fought wars by the side of his master. He has stolen and turned smuggler for man and, because of his criminal acts, met death by bullet or by hanging just as though he were a human who knew human right from wrong.

He has gone into the Roman amphitheater with the gladiators to meet wild bears, leopards, lions. He has fought bulls in arenas. He has even fought other dogs in pits because man so commanded. He has learned difficult tricks to perform on the stage or in circuses to earn money for his owner.

He has tracked down criminals, found lost children, carried messages under fire, and brought help to the wounded. When his owner's sight or hearing failed, the dog has become his eyes or ears.

The beginning of the dog as we know him lies so far back in time that no one can tell when it was or how it happened. Some experts say that the ancestor of the dog was a wolf that prowled over Europe and Asia thousands upon thousands of years ago. Others declare that the dog is a mixture of wolf, jackal, coyote,

and even hyena, for in Africa there are packs of wild dogs spotted like the hyena. They also have the hyena's wide, oval, upstanding ears. In other respects, these dogs resemble a small wolf, measuring about 4 feet from the nose to the end of the bushy tail. But, where the wolf runs in families —mama, papa, children, uncles, aunts, and cousins— the *African "hyena dog"* runs in packs of from sixteen to sixty in number. They sweep over the bush country south of the Sahara Desert, hunting antelope, zebra, and any other animal small enough for them to drag down.

Dholes, the wild dogs of India, also hunt over a vast area, from steaming jungles in the south to the high northern plateaus of Tibet, in search of deer, goats, and wild pigs. Dholes look like red-colored wolves, measure about 45 inches long, including the tail, and weigh around 40 pounds. Like the wolf, they run in families, though they may team up with other packs in order to bring down larger game.

It is said that neither dogs nor wolves will mate with foxes. But they may have mated thousands of years ago, for there are a number

DHOLE

11

ANTARCTIC WOLF

ANDEAN WOLF

RED or MANED WOLF

COYOTE

of dogs that resemble both wolf and fox. One of these is the *Antarctic "wolf,"* first found on the Falkland Islands, on the edge of the Antarctic Continent at the South Pole. Another is a red-hued dog in Ethiopia called the *Simian Fox,* though it is not a true fox. Still another is the *Andean Wolf,* who inhabits the soaring Andes Mountains of South America. The Andean Wolf is gray in color and looks more like a fox than a wolf. Then there is the *Red* or *Maned Wolf* which inhabits the brush country of Brazil and Paraguay. Its size equals that of the large timber wolf but its slender head reminds one of a fox. It is a strange-looking animal, for its legs are so long they are out of all proportion to its short, wolf-coated body.

Wolf, coyote, fox, jackal are all considered as wild

dogs, for they belong to the same group of mammals. This group is called *Canidae* and is part of the order of *Carnivora,* which means animals that eat meat—though they may eat fruit, berries, and grasses, too. Canidae have spread over the world from Pole to Pole. All have similar habits. In a wild state they mate for life and take another mate only when one or the other dies. They are wonderful fathers and mothers. They bear their young in caves or burrows. They hunt in families, in packs, alone, or in couples like the fox. And all of them avoid men. They will follow people out of curiosity, but they take great care to keep out of sight—until their curiosity overcomes their caution.

WOLF FAMILY

The one exception to this is the *Dingo,* the only meat-eating animal in Australia. The rest, like the kangaroo and the koala bear, live on leaves and grasses. The Dingo, some 24 inches tall and 4 feet from nose to the tip of the tail, resembles a small wolf. His soft, furry coat is tawny, rust-red, or black. He, too, hunts either alone or with his family. Though the Dingo is now called a wild dog, authorities believe that he once was tame. They think that he was brought to Australia from the continent of Asia by men in boats. This was more than forty thousand years ago, yet the Dingo seems still to remember the time when he lived with men. Instead of avoiding people, he yearns to be with them and will risk death to join them at their campfires—for, in Australia, white men mercilessly hunt the Dingo because he kills their sheep.

Man, however, made peace with most of the dogs long ago and joined with them in a partnership that has endured to this day. Opinion is divided as to how that partnership came into being. Did man capture and tame the dog or did the dog seek out man? It could very well have been the latter way. After Stone Age man finished his hard-won dinner, he was in the habit of carelessly tossing the scraps outside his cave. To the dog, here was food for the taking.

Man, in turn, saw that the dog could follow a scent far better than he and could out-hear and outrun him in pursuit of game. Sooner or later, he must have studied the dogs that came slinking around his cave and thought, *What if I could use them to help me in the hunt?*

Probably his first act was to steal a litter of pups and raise them with his children. In the beginning, differences among dogs were nature's variations. As litter followed litter, man saw that the pup with the longest legs was the fastest runner; the smallest could burrow best through deep brush; the one with the strongest jaws could hold on to a cornered boar or bear. So he began to breed dogs for special purposes, mating long-limbed dogs to long-limbed dogs, and those with short limbs to those with even shorter ones, until he had just the kind of dogs he wanted.

DINGO

15

IRISH WOLFHOUND

POMERANIAN

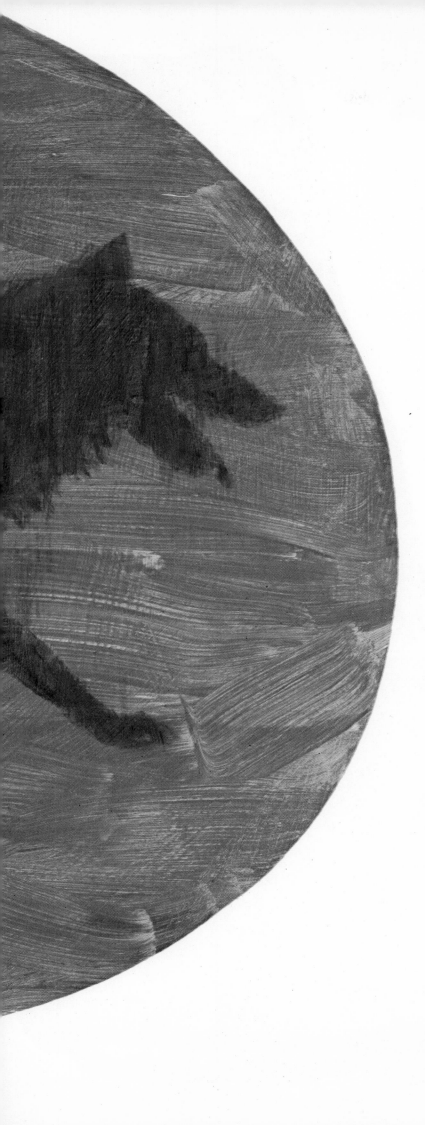

Men have depended upon dogs to such an extent that they have shaped them to perform different tasks needed in different kinds of country and various climates. While man, by careful, patient, selective mating, was concentrating certain desired qualities in one type, he began to keep records of parents, grandparents, and great-grandparents, and to study which ancestors most favorably affected breeding results. These "family trees" are called *pedigrees*. When desired qualities were sufficiently concentrated to produce consistent types, these pedigrees were recorded by the American Kennel Club and that type was recognized as a *registered breed*.

Now the AKC recognizes 116 breeds—from tiny 5-inch Pomeranians to huge 34-inch Irish Wolfhounds —each of which has a Standard of Perfection by which its quality is judged. Dogs who are at least three times judged most nearly perfect specimens of fair samplings of their sex by breeds are designated *champions* and the title *Ch.* precedes their names. Parents and offspring of the same registered breed are known as *purebreds,* the aristocrats of the canine world.

Each dog inherits capacities for the original purposes of his breed—to guard flocks, herds, or property; to scent, point, flush, or retrieve game; or just to be good company. Even if never developed by training, these aptitudes reveal themselves intuitively. Reasons for each dog's particular size or shape, rough or smooth coat, gentle or spirited disposition, reflect the kind of work for which he was bred. When we know his history, we can better understand his needs and his desires. We can come closer to him, deepening and enriching the respect and love that develops between man and dog.

sporting dogs

ALL BREEDS of dogs are divided into six groups by the American Kennel Club. Each group is given a name describing the particular need these breeds fill in the life of man.

The hunting of wild birds that are good to eat, such as grouse, duck, and quail, is called a sport. Dogs that aid in the hunt are known as Sporting Dogs. These are Spaniels, Pointers, Setters, and Retrievers.

The birds hunted by these dogs can be as much of a menace to human survival as are some other forms of wildlife. The average bird eats five times its own weight every day. Although it consumes insects that destroy a farmer's crop, it may also eat the crop. Birds in large numbers can ruin a fruit orchard or a field of grain. And birds multiply much faster than people. If some were not killed, there would be so many birds that they would darken the sky on their migratory flights, as they once did not so long ago. For that reason, certain times of the year have been set aside for hunting them. Enough birds may be killed to prevent them from doing too much damage to crops, while enough will be preserved to keep insects under control.

The sport is in the method of hunting them. Birds have their own ways of protecting themselves. They are so small they can hide in brush and deep grass and in the reeds that edge a lake. Their colors often blend perfectly with their background. If they stand quite still, one can look right at them and not see them. When routed from their hiding place, the birds simply take to the air where humans cannot follow them. Before guns were invented, the birds could sail safely

PORTUGUESE SOLDIER HUNTING
WITH HIS DOG (SIXTEENTH CENTURY)

over the head of the hungry hunter and there was little he could do about it. Occasionally, a well-aimed rock or arrow brought one down. But it often fell back into brush or water and was lost.

Then someone had the brilliant idea of using the remarkable scenting power of the dog to help him. The dog's nose could tell him where the birds were hiding, and it could lead him to the spot where the dead bird had fallen. Experience soon taught men that they could not employ just any dog for this task. Where thick brush and hedgerows grew, it took a small dog to wriggle through the underbrush—a small dog like a Spaniel.

The Spaniel is named for Spain, the country of his origin. There is no record as to when this particular type of dog was first bred. Seventeen years after the birth of Christ, the Spaniel was known as far north as Ireland. There, an Irish king demanded that a certain number of Spaniels be given to him as his royal right. Few dogs were then known by breeds. They were generally classified by the work they did, such as "dogs for the hunting of boars and stags," and "dogs for the hunting of wildfowl." But the Spaniel continued to be known as the Spaniel. In 1386, Chaucer, who wrote the *Canterbury Tales,* mentioned him. By 1557 A.D., the Spaniel was not only recognized for his ability in the field, but for his lovable disposition. In that year, a man named Edgeworth stated, "It is natural . . . to a spaniel to be gentle and familiar."

There was no need to breed fierceness into this delightful little dog. Though he will bark at intruders, he was not shaped to attack, to kill. Nor could he afford to be a "one-man dog," like the Doberman Pinscher. In the old days, several families often lived under one roof. In the castles there were hundreds of people. All these had to be fed. And wildfowl was a source of much-needed fresh meat. So the Spaniel had to be willing to follow anyone who whistled to him.

The Spaniel has hunted with his master all over the world, but it was in Germany, France, and the British Isles where, by crossbreeding, he reached his peak of perfection. There are many kinds of Spaniels. They vary in height and weight, but nearly all have the same general form. Their bodies are strong and compact, covered by a coat of medium-length hair that feathers their legs, their droopy ears, and their bobbed tails. Their coats come in all dog colors, and combinations of colors, except gray. Their muzzles are long enough and broad enough to pick up a fallen bird and carry it back to the hunter. But the first thing one notices about a Spaniel is the dog's eyes. This is especially true of the *American Cocker Spaniel.* His expression is so wistful, so appealing, that it melts all but the hardest hearts.

AMERICAN COCKER SPANIEL

19

The Cocker takes his name from the woodcock, which he likes to hunt. The woodcock is a small bird with short legs and a long bill that nests deep in brush and hedges—the type of country for which the Cocker was bred. As he approaches the bird, he begins to quiver excitedly. In fact, he has been wriggling with eagerness since he first started out with his master before dawn. During the walk through the autumn-dyed woods, across fields touched with gold

AMERICAN COCKER SPANIEL

AMERICAN COCKER SPANIEL

ENGLISH SPRINGER SPANIEL

CLUMBER SPANIEL

by the first rays of the sun, the Cocker has been filled with impatient anticipation. Finally, man and dog arrive at the place where they are to hunt. There is not a sign of a bird, not even a feather. At a signal from his master, the Cocker plunges into the brush. It is not as dense underneath the matted roof as it appears from above. Bird trails run through it. The pheasant often takes to these trails to escape his pursuer. Then the dog has to follow and force the bird into the air where the hunter can get a shot at it. But today the little Spaniel is out for woodcock. Back and forth he dashes, nose to the ground. He is so joyous, so eager, that he makes everything seem like an exciting adventure. And it is exciting. The hunter must follow the dog and be ready to fire in a split second. Suddenly the Cocker picks up the scent. A minute later birds fairly rocket up out of the brush. Instantly the dog drops to the ground so that his master can shoot over his head. Only when he hears the command, "Fetch," does he start tearing through the brush to retrieve the fallen bird—providing the hunter has been lucky.

In general, this is the way all Spaniels hunt, though each has his own pace and method, bred into him to meet the requirements of the type of country in which he is to work. The American Cocker, some 16 inches tall and weighing 22 to 28 pounds, is the smallest and fastest of these "dogs for the hunting of wildfowl." At dog shows these Spaniels are divided into three varieties, which are determined by color: solid black, "ascob," which means "any solid color other than black," and parti-colored.

The *English Cocker Spaniel* is a little more patient, a bit more sedate than his American cousin. And he is from 3 to 6 pounds heavier. Though eager in the hunt, he is happiest when he is with his master. The famous English poetess Elizabeth Barrett Browning had an English Cocker named

Flush. Mrs. Browning was an invalid and spent most of her life in bed, but Flush could not be parted from her. "He loves me better than the sunlight outside," she wrote, thus immortalizing the English Cocker.

Where there are great open fields and vast woods, a light, quick-working dog is best. But where, as in England, there is not as much ground, hunters prefer a heavier, slower-paced dog that will patiently investigate every inch he is set to cover. It is in this kind of country that Spaniels like the *Clumber* and the *Sussex Spaniel* are preferred.

The Clumber weighs some 65 pounds while the Sussex tips the scales at 45. Both measure between 15 and 18 inches at the shoulder. And both take their names from places rather than from the kind of work they do or the birds they hunt.

The Sussex Spaniel was named for Sussex County, in the south of England. This was the home of Rudyard Kipling, who wrote wonderful stories for children. Kipling may have hunted with Sussex Spaniels. This dog differs from other Spaniels in that he "speaks," or "gives tongue" while on the scent. Some hunters claim that this frightens the birds before the men are in a position to shoot. But the natives of Sussex declare that it enables them to keep track of where the dog is working.

The Clumber Spaniel does not need to "give tongue." His snow-white coat, lightly spotted about the head with lemon yellow, makes it easy

SUSSEX SPANIEL

ENGLISH COCKER SPANIEL

to trace his progress. In 1770, the French Duc de Noailles sent some of these Spaniels to the English Duke of Newcastle. The Duke raised and bred them on his country estate, Clumber Park. These dogs have been called Clumbers ever since. The Clumber is especially good at tracking and retrieving pheasants.

The *Field Spaniel* is equally expert in hunting and retrieving large birds, though he generally weighs less than the Clumber. His coat, usually black, is so glossy that it shines. And it is thick enough to protect him when he has to plunge into icy water to bring back a bird or rabbit.

The *English Springer Spaniel* will go after rabbits, too, but he prefers the ruffed grouse and quail. The word "springer" means that he springs or flushes the game out of hiding. All Spaniels do this, but the English Springer was given this name to show that his method of hunting was different from that of the Setters with which he often worked. The English Springer, with his white coat, spotted and splashed with black or red-brown, has long been accustomed to working with a mixed pack of dogs. Somewhere during the centuries, through crossbreeding, he acquired slightly webbed feet, which make him as good at retrieving from rivers and lakes as on land.

FIELD
SPANIEL

BRITTANY
SPANIEL

AMERICAN WATER SPANIEL

IRISH WATER SPANIEL

WELSH SPRINGER SPANIEL

A relative of the English Springer is the perky little *Welsh Springer Spaniel,* who takes his name from the country of Wales. The average Welshman, though loving the hunt, cannot afford a dog for this and a dog for that. He wants an all-around dog that can flush wildfowl and retrieve them no matter where the birds may fall. At home, he expects the dog to have enough good manners to be allowed indoors where he can guard the house. These requirements are fulfilled in the Welsh Springer. Scarcely larger than a Cocker, weighing some 35 pounds, he is a tough, tireless little dog. His thick, silky coat, always white, splashed with red-brown, protects him even in the snows of the rugged Welsh mountains. It may be that, having lived for centuries in Wales, he has become like the Welsh people. He does not take orders easily. And he will not give his trust except to the one who deserves it.

It is a good thing that the *Brittany Spaniel* was given the same name as the province of Brittany in France. At least one can locate the home of this dog. Looking at him it would be difficult to know whether he is a Spaniel or a Setter. He stands tall, 20 inches, and lean, no more than 40 pounds. He wears the Spaniel's wavy coat. The color, snow-white, is touched with orange. But the hair is coarse instead of the usual silk of this breed. His muzzle is longer and heavier, and he has a

stub of a tail. Some Brittany puppies are born without tails. Moreover, he does not spring game. He scents it and then points to where it is hiding. This dog seems to have been shaped for open fields where the wildfowl nest in tall grass rather than in underbrush. In spite of his peculiarities, however, the Brittany is a Spaniel, and as fine a companion as he is a hunter.

The oddest, most comical of the Spaniel family is the *Irish Water Spaniel.* The hair of his coat is twisted into tight curls that are practically waterproof. It stands up in a wild mop on top of his head and grows down in a peak on his forehead. He has hollow cheeks and a rat-like tail. Largest of the Spaniels, he is 24 inches high and weighs 65 pounds. He is too big to work his way through dense cover, but he was not bred for that. Ireland has many marshes and tidal flats, where wild ducks and geese pause to feed and rest on their migratory flights. And against the gray-green of reeds and water, the dark brown of the Irish Spaniel stands out clearly. Highly intelligent, he is easy to train, if that training is accompanied by kindness.

The *American Water Spaniel* is a mystery of the canine world. No one knows how or when he came to the United States. He simply appeared here, shortly after the Civil War. While retaining the color of his Irish relative, his hair is not so tightly curled, nor does it extend to his paws as with the Irish Water Spaniel. It merely fringes the inner sides of his legs. And the American Water Spaniel has no topknot. Eighteen inches high, he weighs 25 to 45 pounds. Everything about him shows that he was bred small enough to work in thick brush and hardy enough for swamps and marshes. He is extremely sensitive to harsh treatment. In a home where he is loved, however, he is completely obedient and loyal.

GORDON
SETTER

ENGLISH SETTER

IRISH SETTER

During the centuries, some Spaniels have had their appearance changed to such an extent that a new name had to be found for them. These dogs were called Setters. This comes from an ancient method of hunting. The dog would scent out the game, point to it, and then "set," that is, sit back while the hunters flung a net over brush or hedge, thereby trapping the birds. Here a small dog would have been a liability. Had he dashed into the brush, he would have sent the wildfowl sky-high before the net could be brought into play. So men bred some of the larger Spaniels to others equally large until they obtained a dog from 22 to 27 inches in height, with a weight from 45 to 75 pounds. In the process, these dogs became longer and leaner so that they could cover the ground more quickly. The hair became shorter and lost some of its Spaniel wave. But the long ears were retained, together with the Spaniel's marvelous scenting power. In fact, this ability was increased until the Setter could take the scent from the air without coming near the concealed birds. There are three Setter breeds. In order of popularity they are: the *Irish,* the *English,* and the *Gordon* (named after the Duke of Gordon).

The Irish Setter loves everybody. In spite of his height, he spends his long life bounding around like a puppy. It is only when he is in the field that he settles down to work. And he can work long hours in country that demands utmost endurance. Away from his native land, some hunters have found fault with him because the gorgeous red-gold of his coat is the same color as autumn leaves, and this makes it hard to follow him by sight. These people forget that the Irish Setter was bred to work in the Emerald Isle. There, against the lush green of Ireland's hills, the Irish Setter shows up magnificently.

The English Setter is a careful, cautious worker. His white coat, marked by small flecks and splashes of black or red-brown, is easily seen in the type of country in which he works. A "one-man dog," he has kept enough of the little Spaniel's wistful appeal to coax his master into letting him have his own way.

Scotland is the home of the Gordon Setter. Among the gorse and heather, his gleaming black coat stands out clearly. A red-mahogany color runs from his throat, under his fine, muscled body, and along the underside of his legs. A dependable hunter, the Gordon's devotion to his master makes him want to please rather than be pampered. He appoints himself stern guardian of the home and family.

If the Spaniels have been world travelers, they are not alone in their globe-trotting. The Pointers can match them country for country. There are Pointers in America, England, France, Portugal, Russia, Spain, and Italy—where a miniature Pointer was bred in the eighteenth century. But Spain was probably their original home.

These dogs are called Pointers because, like the Setters, they point toward rather than flush the game. However, this type of hunting has been raised to a fine art in the Pointer. Bloodhound, Greyhound, and Foxhound gave him such a keen scenting power that he can catch the scent of wildfowl or rabbit from the air twenty or thirty yards away. Greyhound and Foxhound gave him his lean, arched body and his slender legs, built for speed and endurance. Although he is much faster than the Setter, the Pointer's speed does not prevent the hunter from catching up with him. The instant this dog picks up the scent, he seems to turn into a statue. Head pointed toward the quarry, one front leg raised and slightly bent, he will wait without the quiver of a muscle until his master comes quietly up behind him, gun ready. The pointing instinct is so strong in this breed that puppies scarcely have their eyes open before they start pointing—at a rock, a fallen leaf, or the steps of a back porch. Their mother has to teach them what to point at. They already know how.

A Pointer gaining in popularity is the *Weimaraner*, who takes his name from the Court of Weimar in Germany. The nobles first used this dog to track big game. As the larger animals were killed off, the Weimaraner was put to hunting wildfowl. The color of his short-haired coat, ranging from silver-gray to silver-taupe, together with his silent method of hunting, has given him the title of "The Gray Ghost." Perhaps the most remarkable feature of this aristocratic dog is his blue-gray or deep amber eyes—keen, trusting eyes that show his gentle disposition.

In Germany, there are two other fine hunting dogs, the *German Shorthaired Pointer* and the *German Wirehaired Pointer*. These names describe the dogs' coats. The Shorthaired has a beautiful spotted coat of dark brown and white. The Wirehaired is just that—wirehaired. His harsh coat protects him from all kinds of weather as well as entangling brush. A heavy growth of hair prevents injury to his eyes, while whiskers and a short beard keep briers from raking his face.

WEIMARANER

GERMAN SHORTHAIRED POINTER

The idea of producing an entirely different hunting dog came to a young Hollander named Korthals in 1874. Working in both Germany and France, he crossbred such varied dogs as the Otterhound, Setter, large Spaniel, and a rough-coated Griffon. What young Korthals achieved was certainly a different dog. He called him the *Wirehaired Pointing Griffon.* He is a big dog, 19 to 24 inches tall and weighing 50 to 60 pounds. He does point, and he is definitely wirehaired. In fact, his gray-white outer coat stands away from his chestnut-colored inner one like bristles. The

GERMAN WIREHAIRED POINTER

only parts of him that escape this pincushion effect are his droopy, chestnut-hued ears. Though the Wirehaired Pointing Griffon may prove a disappointment in the field because of his slowness, he is a first-class retriever, especially in swamps and marshes.

WIREHAIRED POINTING GRIFFON

Nearly every hunting dog is capable of returning dead birds to his master. But it is not enough for the bird to be found and brought back. A dog must pick it up as gently as he would a live puppy. A crushed bird is useless for food, and so a good retriever must have a "soft mouth," that is, one that will scarcely ruffle the bird's feathers. The experts in this fine art are called Retrievers.

A remarkable feature of Retrievers is their disposition. They are intelligent, gentle, obedient, and never seem to tire of the water. All are around 24 inches tall. Most of them weigh from 65 to 75 pounds. The majority have strong, pointed muzzles, drooping ears, slender bodies, and medium-length tails. They work as well on land as in water. But they were especially bred to retrieve waterfowl, such as ducks and geese. Their coats have a natural oil in them that prevents the water from penetrating to the skin. This keeps them from catching cold, especially when they have had to swim in an icy river to retrieve a dead duck drifting away with the current.

The dog with an almost waterproof coat is the *Curly-*

CHESAPEAKE BAY RETRIEVER

CURLY-COATED RETRIEVER

LABRADOR RETRIEVER

Coated Retriever. It is as tightly curled as the hair of the Irish Water Spaniel—to whom one of his ancestors may have been mated. The *Flat-Coated Retriever* has Gordon Setter blood in him, so his coat is medium-long and flat with a faint wave in it. The colors of both dogs are solid black or brown. The *Golden Retriever* also has a flat coat, but his can be a glorious red-gold. The most versatile of Retrievers, he has a broad muzzle and noble head which give him a kingly look. But his soft brown eyes are as friendly and trusting as a puppy's.

The names of the three dogs just discussed describe their appearance. Others are named for places. One is the *Chesapeake Bay Retriever,* whose history goes back to the American Revolution. The Chesapeake has strange, yellow eyes. His flat, slightly wavy coat is the color of wet dried grass. This blends with the reeds where the Chesapeake lurks, waiting for the wary geese and ducks which he specializes in hunting.

The *Labrador Retriever* is, likewise, named for a place, but the name is a mistake. He did not come from Labrador, though he probably sailed with fishermen who fished off the Labrador coast. The real home of this dog is Newfoundland. His coat is usually solid black, though there are Labradors that are yellow. The distinguishing feature of this fine, intelligent dog is his tail. It is as round and tapered as an otter's. Here is a dog that has been called a Retriever simply because he is an expert in this art. But he has many other virtues, not the least being his lovable disposition.

The latest breed to join the AKC Sporting group is the *Vizsla* or Hungarian Pointer, whose likeness appears in medieval history. He stands 24 inches, has a short, rusty-gold coat, and works well on upland game, rabbits, and waterfowl.

How difficult it is to say, "This dog does this. This dog does that." A dog will try to please, to serve, to aid to the best of his ability. A Spaniel will sit back like a Setter; a Setter will sometimes point like a Pointer. The important thing is to find the birds, the squirrels, the rabbits.

But more than the success of the hunt is the companionship that man and dog find in the open fields, the deep woods, by lakes and streams. Here they become a team. Each depends upon the other. The man ceases to be a master. The dog is no longer just a dog. Man and dog become partners—friends.

GOLDEN RETRIEVER

FLAT-COATED RETRIEVER

hounds

IN ANCIENT times, the boar, the bear, the deer, and the wolf roamed large sections of the world. They were man's enemy and his abundance. They were his enemy because they preyed upon him and upon his sources of food. Deer would strip a barley field overnight. The boar, with the ravenous appetite of the pig that he is, would eat anything. Along with the wolves, he could wipe out a flock of sheep. The boar was also a calf and goat killer. Despite his 500-pound bulk, the wily boar moved like a shadow. Even men on horseback journeying through the great forests that covered most of Europe and the British Isles were not safe from the boar. Wolves did not attack humans unless they were being hunted, but they killed livestock, geese, ducks, and chickens. In those times there was no wire netting. Barriers were made of wood. No matter how high men built fences,

wolves could scramble up and jump over them. No matter how strong he built them, bears could knock them down.

Man soon realized the abundance these predators could provide when hunted down and killed. Deer skins could be cut up for trousers, coats, and shoes. Bear skins became rugs that kept out the cold of the hard-packed, earthen floors. They made soft beds to lie on, and blankets in the winter's cold. Wolf skins served as collars, coats, hoods—even tax payments. According to historical record, a king of England once exacted a tribute from a king of Wales of three hundred pelts a year. Most important of all, of course, they provided food. With the exception of the wolf, all of these animals could be eaten. There being no refrigeration in those days, meat was kept from spoiling by salting it down or cutting it into strips and letting it dry in the sun. Fresh meat was a great treat and eagerly sought by king and peasant alike. But the hunting of it was so difficult and so dangerous that there was never enough of this kind of food.

Here dogs proved most helpful. Man could not keep up with the boar, the bear, the stag, or the wolf. Dogs could. Man could not see these animals when they hid in the forest or the high brush. But the dogs could pick up the scent. It took a small army of men to surround one of these great animals so that it could not escape. A dozen dogs could keep even a boar at bay until the men arrived to kill it. In this way, the dogs helped man. They aided him in finding necessary food as well as skins and hides to keep him clothed and warm. They protected lives and property from the dangerous animals.

BASENJI

Since dogs hunted these animals all over the world, they hunted them in different surroundings and in different climates. For this reason, different types of dogs were needed. And man bred the type of dog that could do the best work in each particular environment.

For example, in Central Africa the elephant grass grew so tall that animals like the springbok or the kudu could disappear simply by lying down. That was where the *Basenji* was needed. He was not used to attack these swift-running animals. His job was to hunt them out, to start them up from their hiding places and point them to where his African masters stood waiting with their spears for the kill.

But even as the prey vanished in these grasses, so did the dog, for he stood only 16 to 17 inches high and weighed about 24 pounds. Yet the hunters had to follow the progress of the dog in order to be at the right spot when the antelope came springing out into the open. They hung little bells around the dog's neck and traced his course by the sound of his chimes. This was especially necessary since this dog was barkless. Because of his habit of leaping occasionally for a glimpse of the long, twisted horn of the kudu, he has been called the "jumping-up-and-down dog." His lustrous-coated, proudly carried body with its prick ears and tightly-curled tail gives the impression of a tiny deer.

Undoubtedly, the Egyptian traders took the Basenjis back to Egypt along with the ostrich feathers and the ivory and the monkeys which they sold in the marketplaces of such great cities as Memphis and Thebes.

The Basenjis remaining on the African plains probably encountered herds of wild dogs. These were spotted like hyenas, with an odd ridge of hair on their backs. Thousands of years later, in the seventeenth and eighteenth centuries, these wild dogs were crossbred with the European dogs such as the Great Dane and the Bloodhound that came to South Africa with the Dutch, the Germans, and the French. The colonists needed a dog to be a guard and companion over their isolated households. This dog must have short hair, otherwise he would be eaten up by ticks. He must have endurance to stand the violent changes of climate. He must have speed and courage to help with the hunting. From these needs the *Rhodesian Ridgeback* was developed. Gone now are the hyena-like spots of his wild dog ancestors. But retained is the ridge of hair in the middle of the back—as well as the fierce courage. A muscular, handsome dog, whose large eyes shine with intelligence, he stands 24 to 27 inches at the shoulder and weighs 65 to 75 pounds. He is a favorite dog of big game hunters. Hunting in packs, these Rhodesian Ridgebacks can attack, and can even bring down, the mighty lion.

In ancient Egypt, lion hunting was a sport of the pharaohs. Here *Greyhounds* were used, not to attack but to corner the animal, to bring it to bay. Once the Greyhound was called a "gazehound." This was because he followed game by sight. The gazelle and the antelope, which he was bred to hunt, were swift prey. He could not take time to trail them by scent. Once he caught a glimpse of them, they were likely to be off and away. So was he. Moreover, he had to be just a little faster than they to run them down. That is why he has such a lean body and long, slender legs. That is why, though standing some 30 inches tall, he weighs only 60 to 70 pounds. His frame is trimmed down like a racer's. It has a deep chest, which arches up into narrow, yet powerful, hindquarters. As do the Basenji and the Ridgeback, he wears a short-haired coat. The Greyhound has traveled all over the known world. His beauty and his slender grace have made him the hunting companion of kings and nobility.

A perfect likeness in form and variety of colors, and

RHODESIAN RIDGEBACK

GREYHOUND

between the Greyhound and the toy Italian Greyhound in size, the *Whippet*—18 to 22 inches tall and weighing 10 to 28 pounds—has been used for coursing rabbits and for racing.

In Egypt the Greyhound has been known for 3500 years. He is a Johnny-come-lately, though, compared with the *Saluki*. This sleek purebred is shown on Sumerian carvings of six thousand years ago. Known at one period as the royal dog of Egypt, his body was sometimes mummified and placed along with the pharaohs in tombs. The Saluki has Greyhound lines, yet he differs from that wind-swift dog in that his coat is soft and silky, his tail and ears feathered. His color is usually fawn or cream, though it can range from white to black and tan. Though lighter and slightly smaller than the Greyhound (averaging between 23 and 28 inches in height and 50 to 60 pounds in weight), he has the Greyhound's slender head and pointed nose as well as his speed. Bred to hunt gazelles, he has long been the treasure not only of pharaohs and rulers of ancient Sumeria, which antedated Babylon, but of the sheikhs

of the desert tribes that wandered from the Sahara to the Caspian Sea, and of the nobility of Europe after the Crusaders brought him home from the holy wars. It is thought that the Saluki was named for an Arab town so ancient that it had disappeared under the sands of the desert before the beginning of written history.

Because the Saluki was both a hunter and a companion to many types of people in many countries, his friendly nature is part of his birthright. He accepts the confines of the home with the same pleasure as he once did the endless reaches of the Arabian desert.

SALUKI

AFGHAN

Another ancient breed—possibly older even than the Saluki—is the *Afghan*. In fact, there are tribes in Afghanistan who claim their Afghan is so old that he represented the dogs in Noah's ark! Archeologists have traced this Afghan back to the Sinai Peninsula, which may have been his original home—the same place where, on Mt. Sinai, Moses received the Ten Commandments.

It is difficult to follow the subsequent wanderings of this dog. He must have crossed Arabia and Persia, but no records of his journey have been found. It is in Afghanistan, a country from which he gets his name, that the Afghan found his true home. Though the plains of Afghanistan are higher than those of Egypt and Arabia, they have the same great space, the same scrub and rock cover for game. First needed to hunt down gazelles, the Afghan later raced deer, as well as hare, in this northern country. As with the Saluki and Greyhound, members of the same family, the Afghan has more height than weight. Standing about 28 inches, he tips the scales at 50 to 60 pounds. His form, too, has been bred for strength and speed. His disposition is a combination of gentleness and courage. He can herd sheep and watch over lambs. On the other hand, working in pairs, he has hunted down leopards and panthers. His appearance is completely different from that of either Greyhound or Saluki. Instead of a short coat, his is long and flowing. The long hair reaches down to his paws and covers the long ears that droop to his shoulders. The hair of his coat is like silk, ranging from white through golden red and fawn to black, with a unique topknot cresting his slender head. This coat has stood him in good stead as a protection from the heat and blowing sand of the plains and the cold of the hills, both in the Sinai Peninsula and in Afghanistan. In the latter country, altitudes may vary from three thousand to over seventeen thousand feet. The hills and the steep mountain passes he had to climb required that he have broad feet and powerful hindquarters. His long, pointed nose winnowed the winds that came down from the peaks of eternal snows as well as the hot breezes that drifted up from the valleys.

BORZOI

The fact that this dog often has attached to his name the word *zai* or "son of" means that his ancestry has been carefully guarded for thousands of years. If any dog can be said to be purebred, it is the Afghan. He has also been known as "monkey-face," an acrobat, and a clown. A tendency toward self-possession does not hide his keen intelligence and understanding.

While the Afghan can live in sub-zero weather, he does not work in the Tibetan heights, nor can he live without protection in the country of deep snows. This was proved when, in the seventeenth century, a Russian duke needed a fast dog for hunting and acquired some Afghans from Arabia. Russian winters soon ended these dogs' careers. He sent for more. By crossbreeding with a dog that somewhat resembled a Rough Collie, an entirely new breed was produced. It was called *Bor-*

zoi, meaning "the swift one." Measuring from 26 to 31 inches in height and weighing from 60 to 105 pounds, the Borzoi resembles the Greyhound but has a long, silky coat of hair. As with the Greyhound in England, the Borzoi breed was at first controlled by the royal family and court. Color took second place to courage and strength in these early Borzois, but white, or white with ghostlike markings were preferred, since they harmonized best with the white gloves of the huntsmen.

In Russia, pairs of Borzoi hunted wolves. In America, he killed coyotes on western plains. Yet he displays no outward sign of his courage and tenacity. Beyond his long, pointed nose, powerful jaws, and short, well-muscled neck, there is no indication of a killer. He looks as though he were bred to adorn the gilded halls of palaces and lie at the feet of kings.

The histories of the dogs of the world have been traced by ancient paintings, carvings, and manuscripts. They have been found in graves and buried in the earth by the action of centuries upon centuries of wind and soil. In just such a stratum have been found the bones of a dog that dates back to 4000 to 5000 B.C. This dog is the *Norwegian Elkhound*. Though Norway claims him, he undoubtedly followed his first Stone Age master across Russia and all of Scandinavia. He was one of the dogs of the Vikings, bred to hunt wolves, elk, and bear —which he still does. But over the ages he has acquired other skills. He will herd reindeer and caribou. He will draw a sled. He protects the home. Slightly smaller than the Siberian Husky and the Samoyed, he measures 18 to 20 inches at the shoulder and weighs about 50 pounds. His head and deep chest resemble a German Shepherd's, but his bushy tail curves over his back as do those of the other sled dogs of the North, and his deep, shaggy coat is as dense as the coats of the dogs of the Midnight Sun. The color is usually black across the body touched with tan which also decorates his head and the underside of his tail.

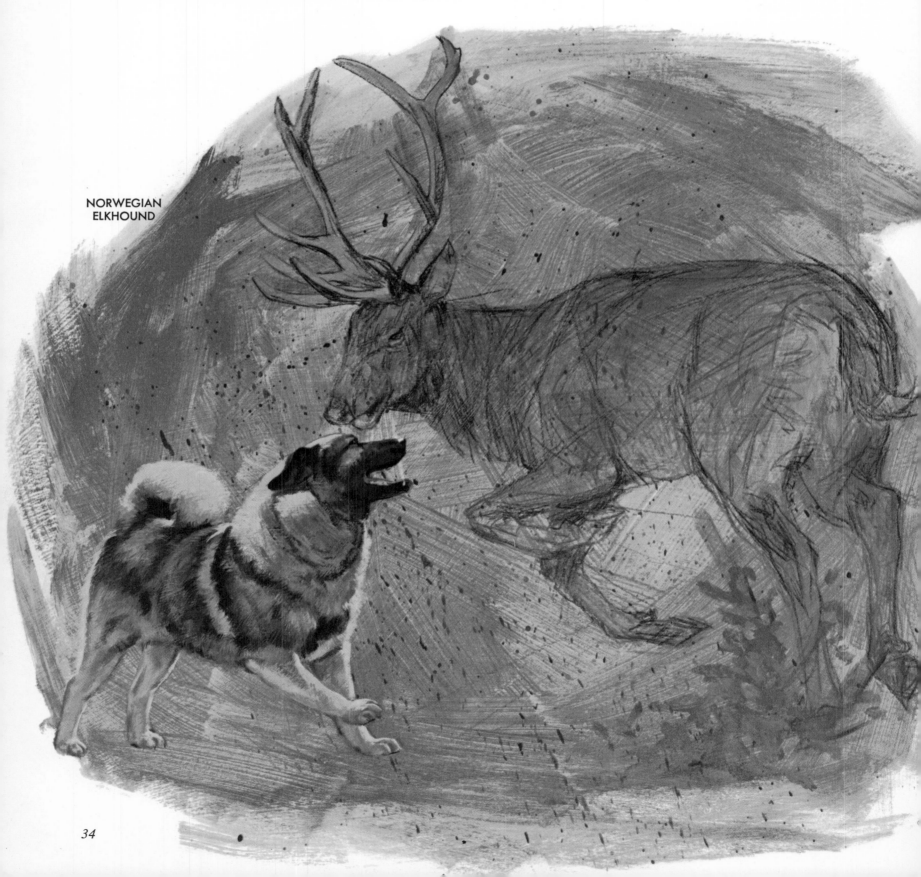

NORWEGIAN
ELKHOUND

The Norwegian Elkhound's method of hunting is unique. He does not chase his quarry. It is too swift for him. He races to cut across its line of flight. Once there, he will charge and, as the great elk's horns sweep down to gore him, he turns and pretends to run away in fright. The challenged elk follows, bellowing until the hills give back the echoes, so eager to reach his attacker that he does not notice that the dog is leading him straight toward the waiting hunters. Should the elk tire, the dog turns and attacks again, and again runs until he gets his quarry within range of his master's weapon. At one time that weapon was a flint-tipped spear. Now it is a gun.

The Norwegian Elkhound is one of the dogs that does not reach full maturity until he is about three years old. He needs this time to develop muscles and intelligence to challenge prey that is among the most savage

the head of Sir William St. Clair that the deer, just escaped from his hounds, would reach the other side of March Burn. Sir William's two Deerhounds raced, baying, after the fleet-footed deer. She had already plunged into the water when they reached her, attacked, and held her, saving Sir William's head and gaining for him the wide lands of Pentland Moor.

This "Royal Dog of Scotland" gradually disappeared from his native land along with the dwindling forests and the Scottish clan system. Fortunately the breed was revived. The present Scottish Deerhound is a close dupli-

SCOTTISH
DEERHOUND

on earth. But during those three years of living with his master and his master's family, another side of his disposition develops. Though he loves to hunt, he is equally fond of home and fireside.

Across the North Sea from Norway is Scotland. Here lives another of the Greyhound family—the *Scottish Deerhound*. A distinct air of breeding and grace about this rough-coated dog recalls those sixteenth-century days when he led his Scottish chieftains through the famed Highland forests on great deer drives. On such a drive a king offered the forest of Pentland Moor against

cate of his ancestor. In color, gray, brindle, yellow, or red fawn, his oversized, Greyhound outline stands 28 to 32 inches at the shoulder and he weighs from 75 to 110 pounds. He has a deep chest and powerful thighs. On his strong neck is a trace of a mane, on the inside of his legs touches of fringe. Otherwise his coat clings closely and is harsh to the touch.

Though dogs are no longer allowed to hunt deer in the United States, the Deerhound will use his legendary talents on wolves, coyotes, even rabbits. Or he will train easily and prove, like any Scot, a loyal companion.

IRISH WOLFHOUND

Ireland developed the most fabulous member of the Greyhound family—a massive dog with Greyhound speed and the strength to bring down a wolf single-handed. He is the *Irish Wolfhound*.

As early as the first century A.D., Celtic bards were singing praises of the great Irish dog. A later manuscript relates the tale of a Wolfhound named Ailbe who defended a whole province. Both the King of Connacht and the King of Ulster desired him, offering six thousand cows, among other things. Finally, they fought a war over him, in which Ailbe died, an even greater hero.

Very early, the Wolfhound began his travels. In the third century, when the Celts sacked Delphi, he arrived in Greece. In the fourth century, a number of Irish Wolfhounds fought in the Imperial Circus, where "all Rome viewed them with wonder." And on Columbus's fourth voyage, an Irish Wolfhound helped him fight off Indians in Panama.

The great dog's fame finally became a hazard to his homeland. He began to seem the only proper present for foreign kings and potentates. While gift dog after gift dog sailed out across the Irish Sea, wolves and stags began to overrun the shamrock country. Ireland had to refuse to export her treasure and keep her Wolfhound at home to perform the task for which he was bred.

Like the too-thorough Scottish Deerhound, these great Irish dogs almost worked themselves right out of existence. When the giant stags and wolves grew scarce in the Irish forests, there was little need for a mammoth Wolfhound. In 1862, a Scotsman, officer in the British army, worked for twenty years crossing the last of the breed with Mastiffs, Danes, and Borzois to bring back the great dog's first stately image.

Today, the Irish Wolfhound is once more one of the mammoths of dogdom. He stands 30 to 34 inches at the shoulder and weighs 105 to 140 pounds. His muscular body has a commanding carriage. His rough, hard coat, shaggy over eyes and underjaw, is brindle, gray, red, black, white, or fawn. He has the keen sight, grace, and speed of a Greyhound and the strength to dispatch a wolf. He is still widely traveled. He hunts lions in Africa, wild boar in Europe, and coyotes and wolves on American plains.

And, being Irish, there is a sweet as well as a fierce side to his nature. He makes as fabulous a companion dog as a hunter. In the home, he has elegant manners and an affectionate nature.

From England came the *Beagle,* the little dog with the big history. It is thought that the Beagle was once known as the *Agassaeus,* one of the famous Celtic dogs imported to Italy along with grain, gold, and silver in the shallow traders' boats with high prows and sterns and great mainsails of painted skins. In the primeval forests of England, the stalwart little Agassaeus ran in the chase with Mastiffs and Greyhounds after elk, deer, even wild boar. He was not expected to race as far ahead as the larger dogs but to pick up the scent and lead the hunters through the tangled underbrush by "giving tongue" in his clear, singing voice. At the kill, while the larger dogs hurled themselves at the maddened animal, the Beagle was right in there racing around and under, nipping at the quarry's legs to further distract it. It was such a life that bred in the small dog its tenacious courage.

The Agassaeus eventually became the Brachet, and then, about the fourteenth century, the Brachet became known as the *Beagle,* from the old French word meaning "clamorous." This name stuck because it suits the dogs well. Their melodious voices when following a scent vary from a deep bass to a bell-like tenor. There are few more exciting sounds than a pack of Beagles in full cry. Probably the most renowned pack of Beagles were the Glove Beagles (5 inches in height) of Queen Elizabeth, known as the Singing Beagles. Each had been carefully chosen so that his "voice" harmonized perfectly with the others.

Now the Beagle is one of the most popular dogs, both as hunter and companion, on both sides of the Atlantic. In the open, he is still famous for his singing cry. Yet within the walls of a house, he rarely barks. On the chase, he plunges wildly through the brush; in the home, when romping with children, he keeps a careful eye on the bric-a-brac. A merry little dog, he is shown and hunted in two varieties, based on size: under 13 inches, and from 13 to 15 inches. His muzzle is short and chiseled, his ears long and expressive. His smooth coat is usually white, patched with black or tan, or both. His joyousness of spirit and a rather searching expression make the Beagle irresistible.

For as long as man has been threatened by larger animals, he has been plagued by smaller ones. And he has bred dogs to help him find and attack these small marauders. He soon discovered that neither speed, sight, nor size in a dog was of much help in following a small animal who moved in devious paths through heavy brush. Only a dog with a nose so keen that he could catch the scent of the fleeing quarry could track down a fox, rabbit, badger, or raccoon.

BEAGLE

BASSET

During the nineteenth century England developed the *Otterhound,* probably from the Southern Hound and Welsh Harrier, because the otters were preying on the fish in rivers and streams. A big dog, standing 24 to 26 inches at the shoulder and weighing about 65 pounds, he has a body resembling a Bloodhound covered with a crisp, hard coat of an oily quality that withstands water. He also has webbed feet to give him a more powerful swimming stroke. In the late nineteenth century packs of Otterhounds hunted regularly through the season. Even today, on the off-season for fox hunting, an Otterhound pack's deep, belling tones can sometimes be heard along a winding brook as they trail their quarry.

Though not widely known as a pet or show dog, the Otterhound is as affectionate in the home as he is fearless on the trail.

The *Basset* from France is one of the oldest of the scent Hounds. A small edition of the Bloodhound, he, too, came from one of St. Hubert's breeds of Hounds of the eighth century, and his scenting powers rank second only to the Bloodhound's. Used for centuries in France and Belgium for trailing small game, he is easily trained. His large Bloodhound head is set on a low, heavy-boned body, 11 to 15 inches at the shoulder and weighing from 25 to 40 pounds. He moves slowly on the trail of foxes, rabbits, or raccoons, doing best in covert hunting and giving tongue with a deep, resonant sound which is easily followed.

BLOODHOUND

OTTERHOUND

Recently the mournful docility of his eyes, his velvety, pendant ears, and his rollicking gait have firmly established this lovable breed as one of America's foremost family pets.

The *Bloodhound* has had quite the opposite experience. Larger than the Basset, measuring 23 to 27 inches at the shoulder and weighing 80 to 110 pounds, he is equally gentle. Yet he has the reputation of being bloodthirsty and ferocious.

Descended from the oldest race of scent Hounds, the Bloodhound came to Europe from Constantinople long before the Crusades, and Norman conquerors brought him across into Britain. From the eighth century on, the famed St. Hubert and other church dignitaries who rode to Hounds are given credit for guarding this Hound strain so carefully that it became known as the "blooded Hound," indicating the purity of its breeding.

England developed the breed for hundreds of years. But it was the United States that adapted to police work the Bloodhound's keen nose and unflagging concentration on the trail. One famed Bloodhound alone tracked down six hundred fleeing criminals, who were later convicted. Human tracking, however, is merely sport for these muscular, black-and-tan, red-and-tan, or tawny dogs with their wrinkled, high-domed heads, their deep-sunken eyes, long, low-set ears, and deep dewlap. When the Bloodhound has finally come up to his quarry, the game is over for him. No instinct tells him to attack.

In fact, no breed enjoys the company of man more than this misunderstood Bloodhound. His affection is boundless and his gratitude deep for any kindness or attention.

The great fox hunters of the world are the *English Foxhounds*. For over three hundred years they have been bred to perfect speed, strength, and tongue. On a frosty morning, a pack of them hot on the trail, racing in full cry over the English downs before a score of pink-coated horsemen, is a fabulous sight.

Once, fox hunting in England was considered mere vermin killing and was often done with nets. Deer hunting was the only real sport. But as deer grew scarce, the king began giving fewer and fewer charters to hunt them. It was then that fox hunting was discovered to be a sport, too, and all Hounds were looked over with a new eye. Crossbreeding began to produce a faster Hound that could match pace

AMERICAN FOXHOUND

ENGLISH FOXHOUND

with the wily fox. Eventually, the breed became a fixed type—the straight-legged, deep-chested, catfooted speedster with "Hound" colors of black, tan, and white, and with bell-like tones. Since that day, breeding records have been carefully kept by the Masters of Hounds, and packs have been bred to suit the local terrain.

American Foxhounds are slighty taller and lighter in weight. They stand 21 to 25 inches at the shoulder, and weigh around 70 pounds, as against the 23- to 25-inch height and 85-pound weight of their English cousins. They were brought to America by De Soto's retainers, and later by George Washington.

Between the Foxhound and Beagle in size, standing 19 to 21 inches, the *Harrier* resembles both. It is used to hunt hare, as well as in drag hunts conducted without live game.

To track badgers to their burrows and then go in after them, German foresters and game wardens developed the *Dachshund* (*dachs* means badger and *hund* means dog). This long-bodied, short-legged, smooth-coated dog is both a scenting trailer and a capsule-sized fighter when need be. The 10-inch, 35-pound Dachshund used for hunting badgers was, by selective breeding, reduced to 20 pounds to enter fox holes; a 7-inch miniature size less than 9 pounds was produced to bolt rabbits. For the cold climate of northern Germany, a *Longhaired* Spaniel-coated variety was developed; more recently a Terrier-coated *Wirehaired* variety was developed to resist bramble and thorn. All three come in standard and miniature sizes. Most common colors are solid red, black-and-tan. Infrequent variations are chocolate, blue-gray and dapple—all with tan points.

WIREHAIRED
DACHSHUND

LONGHAIRED
DACHSHUND

America has produced her own brand of Hound to hunt possum and raccoon—the *Black and Tan Coonhound*. Needed to work in rough terrain, this relatively new purebred combines the bloods of Talbot Hound, Virginia Foxhound, and Bloodhound. He follows his quarry wholly by scent with the unhurried thoroughness of the Bloodhound. But once his coon is treed, he announces it loudly to the hunters by "barking up." An agile, powerful, black-and-tan dog, he stands 23 to 27 inches tall and weighs 55 to 65 pounds. He has the Bloodhound's pendulous ears, but not his wrinkles or excess dewlap. Though he hunts coon for the most part, he has been known to use his skill as successfully on deer, bear, and bobcat.

Once, hunting was necessary for the survival of man. Today, it is a sport beautiful to see, with the fox hunters in their pink coats riding to Hounds on sleek, swift horses. It is a sport because it is often more dangerous to the riders than it is to the fox. The hunters must follow where the Hounds lead. They must jump watercourses and fences, and if a horse falters, his rider may take a spill. But this is a part of the game. Perhaps the fox knows this for he seems to enjoy the hunt as much as the Hounds and the hunters. It is a thrilling adventure for all, and that is why hunt clubs exist in many countries around the world. Though the costumes differ, people are still riding to Hounds as they did hundreds of years ago.

SMOOTH
DACHSHUND

MINIATURE
SMOOTH
DACHSHUND

BLACK AND TAN
COONHOUND

working dogs

WORKING DOGS are those dogs that herd sheep, cattle, reindeer, and caribou. Working dogs draw carts filled with milk cans, cheese, firewood, children, and other small objects. They pull sleds over deep snow and across vast fields of ice. They guard homes, warehouses, barges, docks, department stores. They protect and guide members of the armed forces, the police, and just plain people. From the deserts of Australia to the North Pole, these dogs serve mankind. Throughout the world, working dogs have been given the tasks they can do better than men or that cost men too much in time and energy.

It was once estimated that it would require twelve men to do the work of one *Collie*. Without this dog, bred to herd sheep, Scotland's economy would have been in a very bad way, indeed. For centuries wool was a major product. No one knows the early history of the Collie. The shepherds who owned these intelligent dogs did not care where they came from. If they did their work well, that was all that counted with their masters.

The Collie's name comes from the word *coalie,* which means black. The early Collie was generally black. A scraggly creature he was then compared with the handsome Collie of today. Purely a working dog, he was not expected to win a beauty prize. The turning point in his career came in 1860 when Queen Victoria saw him and liked him. The Collie thus had a royal welcome into society. Soon he was as much at home in England's stately halls as in the shepherds' cottages. His appearance, however, did not match his elegant environment, so his new owners set about to improve him. By selective breeding, they increased his height ten inches, so that he measured 26 inches at the shoulder. His nose was lengthened to aristocratic slenderness. His coat became longer, and the great mane and frill around his neck heavier. Instead of one color, black, he was given a number of colors and combinations of colors for his magnificent coat. The result is the Collie we know today, a dog so regal and beautiful that he has found fame in motion pictures and on the television screen. "Lassie," beloved by millions of children and grown-ups, is a famous Collie.

COLLIE

The long-coated Collies with which we are familiar are officially called *Rough Collies,* to distinguish them from a less well-known, short-coated variety called *Smooth Collies.*

The original, mostly black Collie, which stands about 18 inches tall, is bred as a *Border Collie,* and his skill at herding is demonstrated at some of the largest dog shows. Another dog with a long-haired coat like a Collie, but which is black with tan markings, white feet, and white tail tip, is the *Bernese Mountain Dog,* named for the canton of Bern in Switzerland.

BRIARD

BOUVIER DES FLANDRES

PEMBROKE WELSH CORGI

CARDIGAN
WELSH CORGI

44

The *Old English Sheepdog* looks like a big, shaggy, white-and-gray rug that has gotten up on four feet and walked away. Even his eyes are concealed behind a curtain of hair. But this hair protects his eyes from getting windburned when he faces the gale that sweeps down from the north. Should he turn his back to the storm, there is an extra padding on his rump to keep him warm. He has a lovable disposition because he was not bred to guard or fight. He was bred to drive sheep and cattle to the markets of western England. Even a dog's personality is matched by his breeders with the task he is to do.

Working dogs come in all shapes and sizes. When there is little food, few cows, and not much pasturage, a small dog is needed—small and smart. The Celts brought such a dog with them from Central Europe to the British Isles three thousand years ago. There they settled in South Wales. That is where the *Welsh Corgi* gets his first name. The second name is a combination of *cor,* meaning "dwarf," and *gi,* a variation on the French *ci,* meaning "dog"—Welsh dwarf dog. There are two types of Corgis. The *Pembroke Corgi* has a low-slung, compact body, covered by a coat of short hair. The color may be any of the usual ones worn by dogs. His large, rounded ears stand straight up. His head, broad at the top, narrows down to a black muzzle. He has a stump of a tail just made for wagging. The *Cardi-gan Corgi* is similar to the Pembroke, except that his body and tail are longer. Though the Corgi stands only 12 inches high and weighs about 20 pounds, he is an excellent herder. Unable to control the cattle by an imposing appearance, the "dwarf dog" gets behind them and nips at their heels. By the time the nipped one kicks back, the little Corgi has dropped flat on the ground, and the punishing hoof sails right over him. The intelligence of the Corgi comes from thousands of years of guarding homes, baby-sitting with children, and hunting with men. He has been with humans so long, he seems to think that he is one of them.

Across the English Channel, land and climate are somewhat different from those of the British Isles. For that reason, different types of working dogs were developed—the *Briard* in France, the *Bouvier des Flandres* in Flanders, and the *Belgian Sheepdog* in Belgium. There are physical differences among them. The Briard's head resembles a Skye Terrier. The Bouvier is more like a Schnauzer. Belgian Sheepdogs, which remind one of a wolf, have recently been divided into three breeds. The original name is used for the color black, with small white markings; *Belgian Tervuren* for fawn or mahogany with a black overlay; and *Belgian Malinois* for the dog with a shorter body coat of brindled fawn and a black-masked face.

OLD ENGLISH SHEEPDOG

GERMAN SHEPHERD

This family includes the *German Shepherd*. Authors have tried to list the talents of this particular dog. No sooner have they finished than the German Shepherd presents a new ability. No one knows how many lives he saved when, in World Wars I and II, he served with the Red Cross. With the armed forces, he was a merciless, cunning scout, tracking down the enemy, machine-gun nests, and snipers hidden in the trees. As a messenger, he showed incredible bravery under fire. As a law enforcement officer, he determinedly hunts out criminals. He is vigilant as protector and guard. He is the preferred dog as guide to the blind.

Yet other breeds of dogs have served their countries with the same courage and loyalty. The Belgian Sheepdogs, the Bouvier, the Briard have all done their part. What makes the German Shepherd so outstanding? Perhaps it is because he is perfectly shaped to perform almost any task. Measuring about 27 inches tall, he is neither too large nor too small. Weighing 60 to 80 pounds, he is heavy enough to pull a sled, but light enough to move swiftly. His coat, sufficiently thick to protect him in snow, is not so thick as to hamper him. His fine, intelligent head, with its alertly pricked ears, balances his long, sloping body. His trot is the tireless one of the wolf. He is beautiful enough to challenge the fame of the Collie before the camera in his roles of Strongheart and Rin Tin Tin. To put it briefly, the German Shepherd can do nearly everything any other working dog can do—and do it better.

It seems that the more responsibility given a dog—or a human—the more capable he grows and the more varied become his assignments. When the breed known as the *Great Pyrenees* was first developed, no one could have foreseen that these dogs would become smugglers, or that they would live in Europe's finest palace. The Great Pyrenees was expected to herd sheep—and fight bears. The odd part is that, except for the dog's pendant ears and bushy tail, he looks like a bear. His thick, flat, white coat gives him the appearance of being taller than his 32 inches and heavier than his 120 pounds. He needs this coat in the storms that sweep over the rugged Pyrenees Mountains which separate France from Spain. The coat also serves as camouflage. More than one marauding bear has mistaken the dog for a sheep—to the bear's astonishment.

Often left alone for days at a time to guard the flock, the Great Pyrenees developed a remarkable intelligence. This was put to the test when the shepherds employed them to run contraband goods across the French-Spanish border. With jewels, tobacco, and gold in bags strapped to their backs, the dogs took to trails so high and steep no man could follow.

GREAT PYRENEES

From fighting bears to running contraband to being a pet of royalty is a long leap. But the Great Pyrenees took it in their stride. For years they reigned majestically at the Court of Louis XIV in the Palace of Versailles. There they were called "The White-Furred Lords." They proved to be gentle, loyal companions. And they still are.

The history of the Great Pyrenees is not known. He appeared in Europe somewhere between 1800 and 1000 B.C. Experts are convinced that he does have *Mastiff* blood in him.

Nearly every dog is a citizen of some country. But not the Mastiff. He belongs to time. Sculptors carved his likeness upon the walls of Babylon more than five thousand years ago. They showed him guarding the city gates, the palace, the king. A thousand years later,

MASTIFF

he was guarding Antefaa II, Pharaoh of ancient Egypt. Fifteen hundred years later, the Greeks sent him to Persia as a gift to Cyrus the Great. Phoenicians took him in their high-prowed boats when they sailed to the British Isles looking for trade. There he guarded new masters until Julius Caesar came to conquer Britain. The Romans took the Mastiff back with them, not only to act as guard, but to fight lions, tigers, and bears for the amusement of the brutal crowds that filled the Colosseum. Marco Polo saw him in China at the court of Kublai Khan.

The Mastiff's height of 30 inches and his weight of 165 pounds has enabled him to survive the wild beasts —and the equally dangerous men—he has had to meet in his position as protector of kings and cities. His compact, heavily muscled body is covered by short, stiff hair the color of brindle or fawn. Broad, round-tipped ears hang down on furrowed cheeks. His forehead is deeply wrinkled, giving him a worried look. But he certainly has the right to look worried. Just consider all the re-

sponsibilities he has had to bear for thousands of years.

More than a century ago a cross between the Mastiff and the Bulldog produced a somewhat faster dog for guard duty. The new breed would remain silent at the approach of poachers, would attack on command, and would hold the offenders without injuring them. This breed was named *Bull Mastiff*.

The *St. Bernard* is part Mastiff. This is a dog so identified with the work of rescuing people from death in the snow that one forgets that he was bred to guard. Yet his height, 25 to 30 inches, and his weight, 175 to 210 pounds, show the original intent of his breeders. The Swiss Alpine St. Bernards have a coat of medium length. There is a long-haired type, but these cannot live in the high mountains. Icicles form on their hair and weigh the dogs down until they can scarcely move. So the length of hair may determine whether or not a dog can survive. Both long- and short-haired types are white with patches of red-brown. Both have massive heads. But the St. Bernards' eyes are their most unique feature.

ST. BERNARD

They look so mournful they seem on the verge of tears.

The St. Bernards take their name from Bernard de Menthon, a holy man who became a saint. In 980 A.D., Bernard founded a hospice (a way station for travelers) in a high pass in the Alps. About 1660 the monks who kept the hospice had to bring dogs up from the villages to protect them from roving bands of robbers. The dogs also accompanied the monks when they visited the sick or took food to the poor. It was on these trips, quite by accident, that the remarkable abilities of these dogs were discovered. They can tell, minutes before, when an avalanche is about to fall. Instantly they turn aside from its crushing path. Under these conditions they can follow a trail better than a Bloodhound. They can scent the body of a snow-buried traveler even through deep drifts. These abilities have enabled St. Bernard dogs, working with monks, to save more than 2500 lives. One, named Barry, alone saved at least forty lives. The dogs were never trained to do this. They worked it out for themselves. And how they love to rescue people! They swoop through the snow as though they were playing hide-and-seek.

49

PULI

The same sense of fun is seen in the *Puli*. He is one of three unique dogs that work in Hungary. The other two are the *Kuvasz* and the *Komondor*. The Puli was bred to guard sheep. Medium in size and weight, he has a round head, compact body, and strong, sturdy legs. His almond-shaped eyes give him a squinty look. Every inch of him—from nose to the end of his tail—is covered with thick, shaggy hair. The color may be gray, black, or white. If the Puli is to herd sheep in the daytime, black is preferred. Sheep can more easily see and follow a black dog in the sunlight. White is better at night. So the color of a dog's coat has a reason, a purpose.

The Puli works like a circus performer. He will run across the backs of a bunched flock to get to a straying lamb on the other side. Should a sheep go racing off, the Puli jumps on it and rides it, as a man does a runaway horse, until it can be controlled. People who own the Puli say that he is the most intelligent dog in the world. He does not make friends easily, but when he does, it is for life. And he is so cute, so curious and lively, that he proves to be a lovable companion.

50

The Komondor is a bigger edition of the Puli, reaching a height of 31½ inches and weighing 120 pounds. Authorities say that he came from Russia into Hungary with the Magyar gypsies over a thousand years ago. The Komondor does not herd. He was bred to guard. The important point about this dog is his coat, which grows long and matted. Today it keeps out winter's cold. But once it was a protection against wolves and bears. When a wolf leaped at a Komondor's throat, he often got no more than a mouthful of hair. The coat has only one color; it is white as lambs' wool. This, too, has a purpose. The flock mistake the Komondor for a sheep. Thus they are not frightened when such a big, menacing-looking dog comes among them.

The Kuvasz, too, is white, but his coat is not as long or as matted as the Komondor's. And his muzzle is more pointed. He is also smaller and lighter. Kuvasz is a misspelling of the Arabic word *kawwasz,* meaning "protector of the aristocracy," later becoming *kuvasz,* or "mongrel." For hundreds of years, the Hungarian ruling houses kept this dog for themselves. In the fifteenth century A.D., King Matthias the First depended more upon the Kuvasz to protect him than he did upon his soldiers. Man can be bribed with promises of wealth and power. Dogs cannot. Centuries later, when the common people were permitted to own these dogs, they discovered to their surprise that the Kuvasz was as good at herding as at guarding.

KUVASZ

KOMONDOR

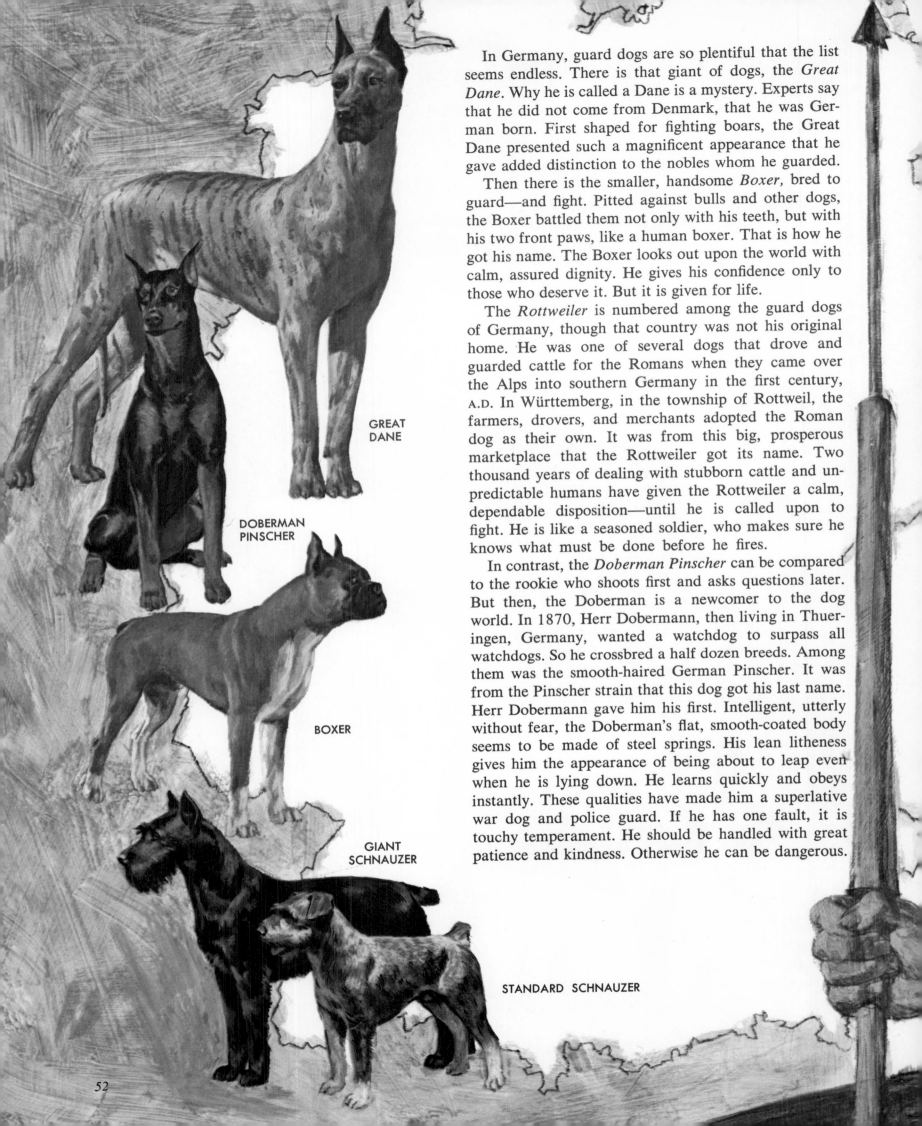

In Germany, guard dogs are so plentiful that the list seems endless. There is that giant of dogs, the *Great Dane*. Why he is called a Dane is a mystery. Experts say that he did not come from Denmark, that he was German born. First shaped for fighting boars, the Great Dane presented such a magnificent appearance that he gave added distinction to the nobles whom he guarded.

Then there is the smaller, handsome *Boxer,* bred to guard—and fight. Pitted against bulls and other dogs, the Boxer battled them not only with his teeth, but with his two front paws, like a human boxer. That is how he got his name. The Boxer looks out upon the world with calm, assured dignity. He gives his confidence only to those who deserve it. But it is given for life.

The *Rottweiler* is numbered among the guard dogs of Germany, though that country was not his original home. He was one of several dogs that drove and guarded cattle for the Romans when they came over the Alps into southern Germany in the first century, A.D. In Württemberg, in the township of Rottweil, the farmers, drovers, and merchants adopted the Roman dog as their own. It was from this big, prosperous marketplace that the Rottweiler got its name. Two thousand years of dealing with stubborn cattle and unpredictable humans have given the Rottweiler a calm, dependable disposition—until he is called upon to fight. He is like a seasoned soldier, who makes sure he knows what must be done before he fires.

In contrast, the *Doberman Pinscher* can be compared to the rookie who shoots first and asks questions later. But then, the Doberman is a newcomer to the dog world. In 1870, Herr Dobermann, then living in Thueringen, Germany, wanted a watchdog to surpass all watchdogs. So he crossbred a half dozen breeds. Among them was the smooth-haired German Pinscher. It was from the Pinscher strain that this dog got his last name. Herr Dobermann gave him his first. Intelligent, utterly without fear, the Doberman's flat, smooth-coated body seems to be made of steel springs. His lean litheness gives him the appearance of being about to leap even when he is lying down. He learns quickly and obeys instantly. These qualities have made him a superlative war dog and police guard. If he has one fault, it is touchy temperament. He should be handled with great patience and kindness. Otherwise he can be dangerous.

GREAT DANE

DOBERMAN PINSCHER

BOXER

GIANT SCHNAUZER

STANDARD SCHNAUZER

NEWFOUNDLAND

Of course, the dog cannot be blamed for this. It was bred in him. Herr Dobermann wanted a super watchdog—and that is what he developed.

Two other well-known German dogs are the *Standard* and *Giant Schnauzer*. They are not guard dogs. The Giant drove cattle to markets in Bavaria. The Standard was a farm-stable helper and an expert rat catcher. The only difference between these two dogs is their size. The Standard Schnauzer is about 20 inches high and weighs from 35 to 40 pounds. The Giant is some five inches taller and 60 pounds heavier. Both have strong bodies covered by a coat of short, wiry hair.

The German word *schnauze* means "muzzle." From this the breed takes its name. It is the Schnauzer's nose that gives him his personality. In profile it looks like a blunt ax that has grown whiskers. A certain honest dignity about them makes them irresistible.

Over the centuries, Europe has sent her dogs to the New World. A Mastiff sailed with Christopher Columbus. It is thought that English settlers brought the Collie with them in colonial times. The *Newfoundland* came over with Basque fishermen.

The Newfoundland is a big dog, with a wide, deep chest. His muzzle is strong and blunted. His most distinguishing characteristic is his flat, thick, oily coat of black hair. The oil aids him in shedding water in which, as a fisherman's dog, he practically lives. Equally necessary is the webbing between the toes of his feet. The Newfoundland loves the water. Even a raging sea cannot daunt him. He has carried lifelines to ships in distress off the Newfoundland Banks. He has rescued an uncounted number of people from the angry waves. He goes out with the fishing fleet and helps the men with their heavy nets. On the land, he pulls barges. He guards the home. He draws carts and carries packs on his back. But the task he likes best is protecting children, whom

ROTTWEILER

he adores. Some authorities say that he may have descended from the Vikings' "black bear" dogs. If so, he also has *Siberian Husky* in him.

The Husky belongs to a family of dogs that spreads across the top of the world, from Norway to Labrador, over Alaska to Siberia. This is the Land of the Midnight Sun, and it is both terrible and beautiful. In summer the sun never sets. In winter it is never seen. Instead, the sky is often ablaze with the rainbow colors of the aurora borealis. Blizzards sweep across endless snowfields and the high, jagged mountains. Icebergs rise above the frozen waters. This is the home of the polar bear, the northern wolf, the caribou, and the reindeer.

Here, all the working dogs have developed strong, compact bodies and thick, double coats to protect them from a temperature that drops to sixty and seventy degrees below zero. They all have "snowshoe feet"—paws thickly padded with hair. The *Alaskan Malamute,* the *Eskimo Dog,* the *Siberian Husky,* and the *Samoyed* so closely resemble each other that it is plain they all had a common ancestor. But who were the ancestors? Some experts say that these dogs descended from wolves. "Not so," insist other authorities. "They are from an ancient, basic type of dog that hunted with the cavemen. There is no wolf in them." Yet they resemble wolves. They have the wolf's wedge-shaped head, pointed ears, and slanting eyes. And the Alaskan Malamute and the Eskimo Dog do not bark; the only sound they make is the wolf's howl.

There are differences, of course, between these dogs and wolves. The wolf keeps his head down as he follows the trail. The dogs hold theirs up. The wolf's tail hangs limply behind him. The dogs carry theirs curved proudly over their backs. The wolf refuses to pull a sled. The dogs are happiest when they are working in harness. Had it not been for the dogs, Admiral Peary would never have reached the North Pole, or Roald Amundsen the South Pole. Dogs helped to open up these vast frozen continents that are now so important to mankind. Plunging through blinding blizzards, across ice fields that stretch from horizon to horizon, Malamute, Husky, Eskimo Dog, and Samoyed hauled the heavy sleds filled with equipment and supplies. They led men around ice that only the dogs sensed might break under their weight. They bypassed deep crevices hidden under the snow. They guided men safely back to home base across snow country where there were no landmarks— just ice and snow, snow and ice.

But these dogs do not just pull sleds. The Siberian Husky and the Samoyed are herders. They herd reindeer and caribou. They are also hunters. They hunt everything on four legs, including the wily, vicious polar bear. Only the Eskimo Dog and the Malamute will not hunt wolves. This, say the Eskimo natives, is because they are part wolf. The Eskimos mate them with wolves. They claim this gives the dogs greater strength and endurance. And, according to them, only a dog that is half wolf can find his way home even when his eyes are swollen shut from snow blindness. Whatever the ancestry of the Eskimo Dog and Malamute, these dogs were not

SIBERIAN HUSKY

ESKIMO DOG

originally household pets. In winter they had to fight the elements every minute to survive. Fighting is instinctive with them, even among themselves. To their masters, however, they are loyal until death.

The Eskimo Dog and the Malamute need their weight—50 to 85 pounds—to draw the heavy loads required of them. The Siberian Husky and the Samoyed are some 25 pounds lighter. If speed is required, men turn to the Husky. It was a team of these dogs that in 1925 brought life-giving serum to Nome, Alaska, when that city was threatened by an epidemic of diphtheria. In the race to check the dread disease, every minute counted. The dogs seemed to know they were racing against time. Led by a Husky named Balto, they plunged on in spite of a terrible storm that roared down from the Pole. A monument in Central Park, New York City, is dedicated to this heroic dog.

The true name of the Husky is *Siberian Chuchi*. He was named after the Chuchi tribe of Eastern Siberia. The bones of dogs resembling the Husky have been found in graves twelve thousand years old. Undoubtedly, such dogs as the Husky and the Samoyed migrated with their masters to Alaska during the last Ice Age.

When the work of the day is over, the Eskimo Dog and the Malamute are left outside to sleep in the cold, regardless of the weather. Their only association with people comes when they are harnessed to the sled, and when their masters throw them chunks of frozen fish or walrus meat. The Chuchis, however, took their dogs into their tents. This association has given the Siberian

Husky the experience necessary to make him a companion as well as a guard.

But the most remarkable of the northern dogs is the Samoyed. Where the others are colored brown, fawn, black, or wolf-gray, the Samoyed, sometimes called the Christmas dog, is snow-white or cream. He was a pet of the Samoyed tribe whose members range across the tundra between Siberia's Yenisei River and the White Sea. Some time in the far past, these gentle people may have lived in Central Asia. Driven out by the more warlike tribes, they journeyed north until they reached a land so desolate that their pursuers had no wish to follow them. Here their dogs helped them to survive. They herded reindeer for their masters. They hunted with them. They guarded their children and their possessions. The dogs even provided clothing for them. The outer coat of the Samoyed is thick and rough, but the inner one is soft. The combings from this inner coat can be woven into warm cloth. In turn, the Samoyed natives cherished the dogs, counting them among their most valuable possessions.

It has been said that a dog is what you make of him. He seems to take on the characteristics of his master, to mirror his moods, his personality. The Samoyed is all gentleness and kindness. He loves people, and shows it from the tip of his bushy, curved tail to the end of his muzzle, where the mouth, turned up at the corners, seems to be always smiling.

Other Working breeds advancing toward AKC recognition are *Akitas* and *Australian Cattle Dogs,* as well as the Border Collies already described.

ALASKAN MALAMUTE

SAMOYED

SCOTTISH TERRIER

terriers

EXPERTS SAY that the special kind of dog known as Terrier was first bred in the British Isles. But one would have to go back several thousand years to catch a glimpse of the beginning of these dogs. Since then, Terriers have made themselves useful in nearly every country on earth. They may be rightly called canine citizens of the world. Because the enemies which they were bred to fight are generally the same everywhere, Terriers have not been compelled to change either in shape or disposition, regardless of where they have worked.

The one exception to this is the *Australian Terrier,* and his change was merely to improve the strain. However, as the crossbreeding took place in Australia, he was given the name of the country of his birth. He is an adorable little dog, 10 inches in height, weighing from 12 to 14 pounds. A little longer than he is tall, he is capable of many tasks. Aside from being a hunter of small game, he has guarded mines, tended sheep, and is an effective watchdog. The straight, coarse hair of his shaggy coat is colored either blue-black with tannish-red markings or a solid red. Small, pointed or slightly rounded ears stand up on either side of a broad, intelligent head. These, together with a stub of a tail, carried high, give the Australian Terrier a look of perpetual eagerness to be off and doing something. In a large measure, this is true of all Terriers. The ability to move with lightning speed has, alone, saved their lives.

To understand why the Terrier was bred to be the kind of dog he is, one must know the habits of those vermin and small animals with which this type of dog has had to battle. All foxes, hares, rabbits, otters, rats and mice, finding themselves in danger, go to ground. That is, they disappear into some kind of hole, usually a burrow deep in the earth. Hounds can pursue a fox as long as it is out in the open, but when it dives into a burrow, with a pert flit of its tail, all a Foxhound can do is stand around the entrance helplessly barking. Then the Terrier is brought in. Most of these dogs, too small to keep up with the chase, are carried by the hunters until the fox does its disappearing act. At this point, the Terrier is turned loose, to plunge eagerly down into the burrow. Most burrows have several exits, and the Fox Terrier's assignment is to bolt the fox, so that the hunt can continue.

The Latin word *terra* means "earth." In short, Terriers are earth dogs, dogs that go to ground after their prey. There, in the dark depths of the earth, a terrier needs courage and skill, possibly to fight to the death.

Breeders of *Scottish Terriers* declare that their dog was the original Terrier, once called the *Aberdeen*. But as this claim is made by the admirers of the *Skye Terrier*, the *Lakeland*, and the *Border*, it is best to ignore the problem of which came first until some record is found that will definitely settle the argument. Certainly, the Scottish Terrier has a long history. Six Scotties were sent as gifts to France by King James I of England in the seventeenth century.

The Scottie looked about the same then as he does today. His moderately short body is carried on heavy, stubby, slightly bent legs. The bend in the legs gives him the rolling walk of a sailor. But their shape and power allow him to scramble down a burrow as fast as a fox or a badger. His rough, double coat—that can be black, wheaten, or dark gray in color—keeps him from being raked by the sharp edges of rocks on his way down the tunnel. His almost square muzzle is covered with hair to protect his nose. His ears are short and perky. Perky, too, is his small, fuzzy tail. He is one of the most independent dogs on earth. If the buyer of a Scottie realizes this, he will wait until one of the puppies out of the litter chooses *him*. Otherwise, the little dog may give his master loyalty, but defer his love.

Courage is the outstanding quality of all Terriers. It takes an enormous amount of courage to follow a fox, an otter, or a badger into its burrow and do battle in the dark with an enemy that is often larger than the dog. The Red Fox, for example, measures about 16 inches at the shoulder. Full grown, it is large enough to kill a lamb or a young calf. Cleverness is bred into it and, when cornered, it is a vicious fighter.

It is difficult to understand how such a small, winsome dog as the Skye Terrier could stand a chance

AUSTRALIAN TERRIER

against a fox. The Skye is almost lost in a coat of straight, thick hair. It sweeps down to the ground, over his face, and forms a beard under his chin. Out of this covering—which can be any color from black to cream—large ears stand erect and small, dark eyes peer mischievously. Yet natives of Skye, that craggy island off the northwest coast of Scotland, have depended upon this diminutive dog for hundreds of years. His bravery inspired the Skye Club of Scotland to take as their motto: "Who dares meddle with me." The devotion of the Skye Terrier to his owner has been immortalized in the story of Greyfriars Bobby, who for ten years stood guard over his master's grave. As a hunter, the Skye, small though he is, has won many a duel with the wily fox.

When in strange country, the fox usually travels in a straight line and is easy to catch. On home ground, however, it knows every hole, cave, and crevice between rocks—and this is where the *Cairn Terrier* enters the picture. *Cairn* means "rocks," but not just any jumble of rocks. A cairn is a cone-shaped pile of stones erected to the memory of some important person. In the Highlands of Scotland, they are memorials to the chiefs of various clans, and there are many of them. Rain and wind loosen the crevices between the stones, and soon there is a space large enough for Master Fox to slide through. And right after him goes the Cairn Terrier, for this smallest of Terriers was bred to wriggle his way between just such stones.

Ten inches high, weighing 13 to 14 pounds, the Cairn has the usual double coat worn by all shaggy Terriers. The colors run from sandy through red, and from gray to black. His muzzle is not as squared off as the Scottie's, though he has the same upstanding ears and short tail. Nor is the Cairn as dignified as his dour cousin. Merriment gleams in his large, dark eyes while his good-natured charm belies his fighting spirit.

One cannot mention the Cairn without including the

WEST HIGHLAND WHITE TERRIER

West Highland White, for some authorities claim that this Terrier was merely the odd puppy in a Cairn litter. It was once thought that the better a Terrier's coat blended with the Scottish heather the more difficult it would be for a rabbit or badger to see him. So when a white puppy appeared, it was promptly killed as being worthless. The Malcolms of Poltalloch in Scotland thought otherwise, and they began to collect and breed them. To everyone's surprise, the snow color of the "Westie's" coat did not prevent him from being as successful a fighter as the Cairns or Scotties. Moreover, the West Highland White proved the gayest of dogs, always ready for a romp. An added appeal is this small dog's face, which retains its appealing baby look even after he is grown. He is at home both on the farm or in a modern apartment. But if there is any ground around, he will

dig in it. This may exasperate the gardener, but the dog cannot be blamed. After all, he is a Terrier, an "earth dog."

No dog, however, can dig as fast as a badger. Its powerful front claws can outdig a strong man wielding a shovel. Though the badger kills rodents, it also kills any small game that comes along. As these include ducks, chickens, geese, and wildfowl, a badger in the neighborhood endangers much of the fowl intended for the family table. Once run to ground, the badger turns over on its back to fight. This position enables it to use its ripping claws. The Terrier that survives these claws will bear the marks of them all his life.

The *Sealyham* has often met this deadly enemy and vanquished it. Unlike the Scottie, Skye, Cairn, and West Highland White—all as Scottish as a clan plaid—the Sealyham was bred in Wales about a hundred years ago. Sealyham is the name of the estate of a Captain John Edwardes, who wanted a dog with as much strength and courage as could be stuffed into a body small enough to go into a burrow. His desire was fulfilled in the little Sealyham. His rough, double coat is all white though there may be tan markings, especially around the head and ears. The shape of his long muzzle is almost lost under whiskers and beard. The unique characteristic of this dog is the shape of his legs. Thick and stumpy, they look as though they had been cut off at the knees. When he wants to, the Sealyham can act the clown. But he can also show a disdainful dignity that says clearly, "Hands off." His coat needs frequent grooming, an attention he loves.

In contrast, the straight, rough coat of the *Norwich Terrier* has only to be brushed to be kept in shape. Its

SKYE TERRIER

CAIRN TERRIER

SEALYHAM TERRIER

general color is fox-red, but it can be black or tan. The Norwich Terrier was named for the ancient city northwest of London. It was here this little dog first saw the light of day. He stands 9 to 12 inches tall and weighs 10 to 14 pounds. He has a well-shaped, round head, and his docked tail provides a good handhold to pull him out of a burrow. Though his large, pointed ears may stand up or flop down, in either position they seem to be continually listening for the scamper of rats or the patter of a rabbit. In fact, it was to rid the country of these two pests that the Norwich Terrier was bred.

Rabbits multiply at an alarming rate. They begin to breed at six months, produce from four to eight litters a year, and, if unmolested, live for seven or eight years. Australia exported in one year 70 million rabbit skins. These are used for furs and in the making of hats. No vegetable garden is safe from these pests, as Mr. MacGregor discovered in the story, "Peter Rabbit." They live in burrows and dive back into burrows at the slightest sign of danger. They move so fast that the pursuing dog must be even faster just to catch up with them. Here the Norwich Terrier shows an unbelievable endurance. And, if one could ask this little dog what he thinks he could fight, other than rats and rabbits, he would probably reply promptly, "Anything on four legs."

Another game fighter is the Border Terrier, who comes from the Cheviot Hills that mark the boundary between England and Scotland. He is not as handsome or as endearing in appearance as some of the other Terriers, but his disposition makes him a wonderful companion. He measures 10 to 12 inches in height and he weighs from 11 to 15 pounds. The color of his rough, double coat is reddish or like ripe wheat. His head somewhat resembles that of an otter. His ears flop and his medium-length tail curls up like a scimitar. Aside from fighting foxes, the Border Terrier herds sheep and cattle and is an excellent watchdog. The most remarkable thing about the Border is his lack of possessiveness, a trait usually found in most Terriers. The Border loves children and will even tolerate cats.

Though the shape of the Border Terrier's head may remind one of an otter's head, it is the *Dandie Dinmont* that was bred to fight this dangerous, slippery enemy. Otters live near woods and lakes, where they dig burrows into the sides of the banks. Though preferring to travel by water, on land they can outrace a running man. Their appetite for fish and frogs will strip a lake of its aquatic life. For this reason, they are a menace to people who need this food for their own existence. The otter, member of the weasel family, is a wicked fighter, going for the throat of his attacker. The thick hair that bushes the funny face and throat of the Dandie Dinmont must discourage the otter that gets tangled up with it.

This Terrier received his name from a book, *Guy Mannering,* written by Sir Walter Scott. In it, there is

LAKELAND TERRIER

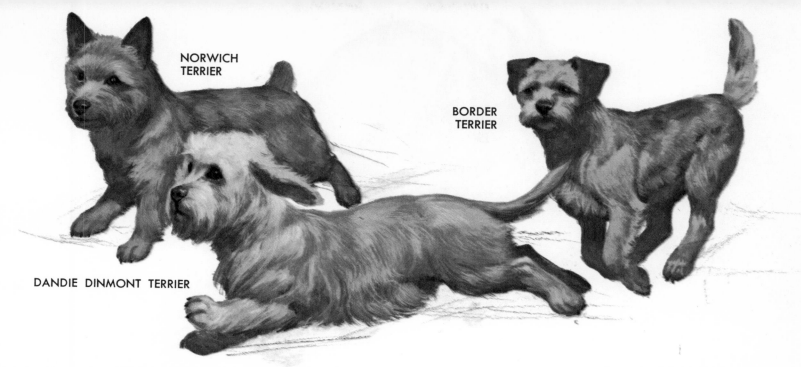

NORWICH TERRIER

BORDER TERRIER

DANDIE DINMONT TERRIER

a character called Dandie Dinmont, who was so proud of his dogs that he continually boasted about them. People began calling this type of Terrier a Dandie Dinmont, and the name has been retained to this day. The Dandie neither looks nor acts the savage foe of predators he really is. Rather, he is a comic picture of a dog. His forearms are shorter than those in many breeds—making burrowing easier. He weighs from 14 to 24 pounds, though he measures only 8 to 11 inches. His thick coat of crisp hair is either mustard or pepper in color, with the light part centered around his broad head and under his body. His droopy ears are set so low that they touch his cheeks. Eyes, large and round, seem to regard one with a flat, questioning stare, as though saying, "I don't remember ever meeting *you.*" The next instant he may whip into a series of such clownish antics that one cannot keep from laughing. Like the Border Terrier, the Dandie Dinmont forgets all his fighting heritage when he is with children, whom he adores.

The *Fox Terrier,* however, demands the same devotion he gives to the one he loves. Taller than the Dandie by from 3 to 5 inches, weighing some 18 pounds, this Terrier is bred and shown in two coat varieties. The *Smooth Fox Terrier* has a flat, hard, dense coat, while the *Wirehaired Fox Terrier* has a harder, wiry coat. Both are white in color, marked with patches of black or tan. As companion to horses, the Terrier often sleeps in their stalls. When not fighting the fox that has gone to ground, this Terrier is a gay companion—as long as he is the center of attention.

The Lakeland Terrier was also bred to battle foxes, though he is equally good at fighting otters. He takes his name from the Lake District in the north of England where there are seventeen lakes of various shapes and sizes. Wild, beautiful country, it is a paradise for both land and water predators. The Lakeland Terrier is about the same height as the Fox Terrier. He, too, wears a wirehaired coat, though the colors range from light wheaten or straw-colored tan to blue, black, or liver, with or without tan markings. The small, button ears and jaunty tail of the Lakeland are similar to the Fox Terrier's.

In fact, the Fox Terrier lines can be clearly seen in many Terriers, such as the *Welsh,* the *Irish,* and the *Kerry Blue*—all of them rugged fighters and cheerful

WIREHAIRED FOX TERRIER

SMOOTH FOX TERRIER

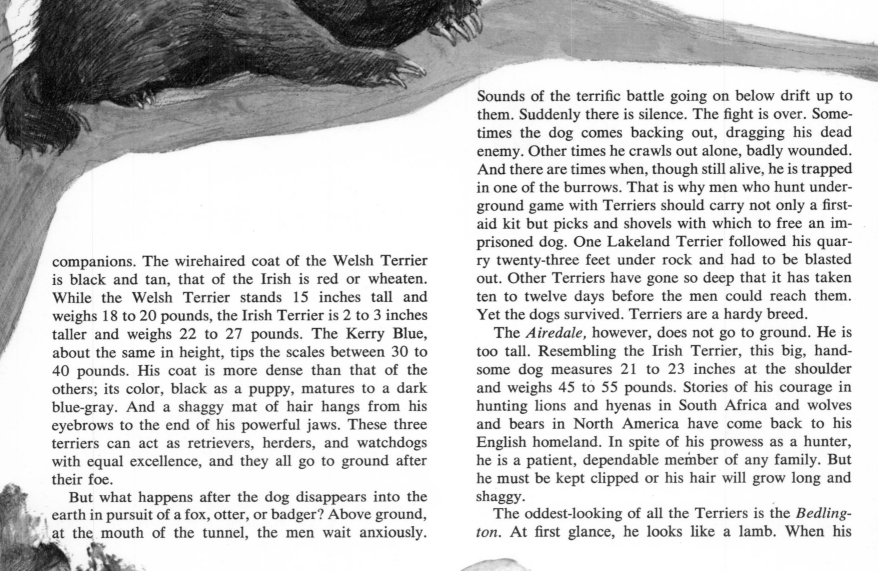

companions. The wirehaired coat of the Welsh Terrier is black and tan, that of the Irish is red or wheaten. While the Welsh Terrier stands 15 inches tall and weighs 18 to 20 pounds, the Irish Terrier is 2 to 3 inches taller and weighs 22 to 27 pounds. The Kerry Blue, about the same in height, tips the scales between 30 to 40 pounds. His coat is more dense than that of the others; its color, black as a puppy, matures to a dark blue-gray. And a shaggy mat of hair hangs from his eyebrows to the end of his powerful jaws. These three terriers can act as retrievers, herders, and watchdogs with equal excellence, and they all go to ground after their foe.

But what happens after the dog disappears into the earth in pursuit of a fox, otter, or badger? Above ground, at the mouth of the tunnel, the men wait anxiously.

Sounds of the terrific battle going on below drift up to them. Suddenly there is silence. The fight is over. Sometimes the dog comes backing out, dragging his dead enemy. Other times he crawls out alone, badly wounded. And there are times when, though still alive, he is trapped in one of the burrows. That is why men who hunt underground game with Terriers should carry not only a first-aid kit but picks and shovels with which to free an imprisoned dog. One Lakeland Terrier followed his quarry twenty-three feet under rock and had to be blasted out. Other Terriers have gone so deep that it has taken ten to twelve days before the men could reach them. Yet the dogs survived. Terriers are a hardy breed.

The *Airedale,* however, does not go to ground. He is too tall. Resembling the Irish Terrier, this big, handsome dog measures 21 to 23 inches at the shoulder and weighs 45 to 55 pounds. Stories of his courage in hunting lions and hyenas in South Africa and wolves and bears in North America have come back to his English homeland. In spite of his prowess as a hunter, he is a patient, dependable member of any family. But he must be kept clipped or his hair will grow long and shaggy.

The oddest-looking of all the Terriers is the *Bedlington.* At first glance, he looks like a lamb. When his

BEDLINGTON TERRIER

WELSH TERRIER

IRISH TERRIER

KERRY BLUE TERRIER

AIREDALE TERRIER

dense, linty coat is more blue-gray, the resemblance is more striking than when it is dark brown or light tan. Little bunches of hair tassle the ends of ears that are set low on his slender head with its pointed muzzle.

Bedlington is the name of a coal mining district in Northumberland, close to the border of Scotland. The miners here were not interested in dogs that could go to ground, for the men went to ground themselves every day in tunnels deeper than any animal could burrow. What they wanted in their leisure time was a small racing dog. To achieve this, a Whippet was crossed with a Dandie Dinmont Terrier. Whippet blood in the Bedlington gives him his speed. The Dandie strain makes him an excellent ratter.

Rats are deadly to the health and well-being of people. Even today, in the United States, where corps of vermin exterminators are hired to kill these pests, the damage caused by rats costs hundreds of millions of dollars every year. Rats will eat anything—the grain the farmer has planted, the food the housewife has stored in the kitchen. They travel in ships all over the world. In their journeys, they have carried deadly diseases through the fleas that infect them. Bubonic Plague is one of these diseases. This plague has been called Black Death. In Europe, in 1347, it killed one fourth of the population. As far back as the memory of man goes, he has been fighting rats. And dogs have helped him—such dogs as the Bedlington, the *Miniature Schnauzer,* and the *Manchester Terrier.*

The Miniature Schnauzer resembles his two larger brothers, the Giant and the Standard Schnauzer. His height is from 12 to 14 inches, his weight around 15 pounds. It may seem strange that a rat-killing dog must have the same courage as one that goes after the fox, badger, or otter, but a cornered rat is extremely ferocious. Moreover, it was considered a sport to let as

many as a hundred rats into a pit for a single dog to fight while the onlookers bet on how many a favorite dog could kill within a given time.

One of the most expert ratters is the Manchester Terrier. Manchester, now a city of modern factories, has a history reaching back to the Roman conquest of Great Britain. Rat killing and rabbit coursing—setting fast dogs to chase a rabbit—were once the favorite sports of working people of Manchester. The *Standard* variety, 12 to 22 pounds and 13 to 16 inches tall, excels in both these fields. Like the Bedlington, the Manchester has Whippet blood in him, giving him his lithe, graceful body as well as his speed. That he also descends from the Black and Tan Terrier is shown in his black, satin-smooth coat, touched with a rich, red brown. His drooping ears frame sparkling dark eyes, and his long, pointed muzzle is a perfect instrument for rat catching.

All Terriers are fighters, but some, like the *Staffordshire* and the *Bull Terrier,* were bred to fight each other in wooden pits set into the ground, where they could

MINIATURE
SCHNAUZER

STANDARD
MANCHESTER
TERRIER

do battle without endangering the watching audience. The Bull Terrier, 17 to 22 inches high and from 25 to 60 pounds in weight, is the result of crossbreeding a Bulldog with a white English Terrier, a dog now extinct. The Bull Terrier's long, slender nose gives him an aristocratic look, which is emphasized by his sleek, white coat. So great was the courage of this dog in the ring, so elegant his appearance, that he was given the title of "the White Cavalier." Bull Terriers have two color varieties: *White* and *Colored,* which may be any color but white, with brindle preferred.

Of equal Bulldog and Terrier ancestry, the Staffordshire Terrier has neither the grace nor elegance of the Bull Terrier, but he has the same flaming spirit. His cropped, pointed ears are set behind a broad forehead. His medium-long jaws have a crushing power. Standing 17 to 19 inches at the shoulder, he weighs between 35 and 50 pounds. His smooth coat comes in any color or combination of colors. Staffordshire, which gave this dog his name, is rich in coal and iron. Here the miners secretly pitted their Terriers against each other long after that cruel sport was forbidden by English law.

Soft-coated *Wheaten Terriers* and *Tibetan Terriers* are presently qualifying for the AKC Terrier group.

Centuries ago, the art of reading and writing was the privilege of the wealthy, the leisure classes. For that reason, few records were kept of these dogs. Then, too, they were often used to run down small game on private estates. And no one boasted about any poaching his dog did by the light of a full moon.

Perhaps it was living in constant association with their masters that gave these dogs a dual personality. One side of their nature is that of the fighter. The other side is gay, fun-loving, at times even comic. Hardy, needing little care, Terriers can take punishment that would kill an ordinary dog, and then get up, shake themselves, and walk off. Their loyalty and devotion, though sometimes causing them to suffer from jealousy, is so great that they are willing to die for their masters. The courage and jaunty spirit of all Terriers have made them loved and admired companions the world over.

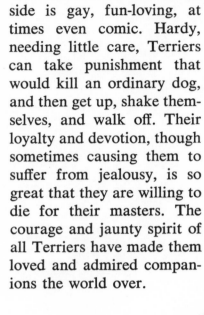

STAFFORDSHIRE TERRIER

BULL TERRIER

MALTESE

POMERANIAN

toy dogs

LOOKING BACK over the histories of the various breeds of dogs, one can understand their usefulness to people and where they fitted into human lives. But what of the Toy dog?

The *Pomeranian* is from 5 to 7 inches high and weighs 3 to 7 pounds. He looks like an animated powder puff. His fluffy, double coat comes in many colors and combinations of colors. His beautiful, plumed tail is carried over his back. He has what is called a "spitz" face—that is, a slender, moderately pointed one. His brown eyes fairly gleam with intelligence. He learns obedience quickly and easily. Though a Toy, he is ready to accept any challenge, apparently thinking he is still a big sled dog, as his ancestors were in Lapland. These dogs were

not called Pomeranians then. They received this name when, in their travels, they reached Pomerania, a part of ancient Prussia. It was here, through selective breeding, that they were reduced from their original size to the tiny mites they are today.

Why should humans take useful, working dogs and shrink them until they can be carried in a lady's hand or a man's coat pocket? Their smallness prevents them from doing anything except barking. They would make no more than a mouthful for the prey they once fought. Today, the Pomeranian's enemies are not the gray, arctic wolves. They are little children who pull his hair—the same type of hair that once kept his great-great grandfather warm in sub-zero snowstorms.

What is the purpose of Toys? This is not a recent movement to produce small dogs to fit into small, modern apartments. Toys have been bred for thousands of years and have been cherished by men as well as women.

One such Toy is the *Maltese,* who takes his name from the island of Malta, in the Mediterranean. The Maltese is a shaggy little dog measuring 5 to 12 inches and weighing about 3 to 7 pounds. His black button nose and dark, eager eyes peep out from a long white coat that completely covers him. His lineage goes back so far that his likeness appears on antique Greek vases. When the Apostle Paul was preaching in Rome, a governor of Malta was having a picture painted of his Maltese by a then famous artist. The dog's name was Issa, and his owner adored him.

Toys have been a part of written history. A *Papillon* was a favorite of Marie Antoinette, Queen of France. This little, Spaniel-type dog weighs up to 10 pounds and measures 8 inches at the shoulder. Though his coat is medium short, it deepens into a thick collar around his neck and hangs down below his chin like a Santa Claus beard. Aside from these touches of white, his color may be black, or may range from tan to red. The face of the Papillon is slender. He has large, bright eyes, and his full ears, pointed at the tip, stand gaily erect. They are so delicately fashioned that Marie Antoinette likened them to the wings of a butterfly. The French word *papillon* means "butterfly." Perhaps when no one was looking the Papillon caught a few rats in the Palace of Versailles, but he was not bred to be a ratter. He was bred to be a comforter. He comforted France's beautiful Queen on the way to the guillotine during the French Revolution, just as an *English Toy Spaniel* comforted Mary, Queen of Scots, during her long imprisonment in the Tower of London. When at last she mounted the scaffold to meet her executioner, this little 10-inch-high dog went with her, hidden under her long skirts. A pair of black-and-tan Toy Spaniels were so cherished by King Charles II of England that this particular variety has been called *King Charles* ever since. Other varieties are solid chestnut red *(Ruby),* red and white *(Blenheim),* and white, black, and tan *(Prince Charles).*

PAPILLON

YORKSHIRE
TERRIER

CHIHUAHUA

Toy Poodles are pocket-sized replicas of the Miniature and Standard varieties described among the Non-Sporting breeds. The Toy variety is limited to 10 inches in height and appears in a variety of solid colors.

The Poodle's coat is easy to keep in shape compared with that of the *Yorkshire Terrier*. He is a cross between the Skye and several other Terriers. His name comes from Yorkshire, in the northern part of England, where his ancestors were used to catch rats. The Yorkshire measures 8 inches tall and weighs some 4 to 8 pounds. He has a sturdy body and a coat of straight, silky hair. Puppies are born black, and their color matures to an exquisite steel-blue with markings of golden tan. With ordinary grooming, the coat is no problem; if cultivated for show competition on waxed-paper curlers, it can grow long enough to trail on the ground, topknot tied back with hair ribbons. He has the spirit of all Terriers, ready for fun or fight, though he is quite helpless to protect himself. But that is a part of his charm—as it is with all Toys.

These minute dogs are completely dependent upon humans. Owning a Toy is like having a baby in the house. They demand constant attention. That is why they are called comforters. They keep people from thinking too much about themselves. One's worries tend to disappear when one is busy combing, brushing, exercising, feeding, and cuddling these diminutive pets. So small that they cannot safely play with other dogs, they insist that people play with them. In that play, a person's deepest sorrow may vanish, and the world does not seem so dark.

TOY POODLE

PEKINGESE

The large, protruding eyes of the *Chihuahua* hold the look of a lost, bewildered orphan. They melt all but the hardest hearts. Weighing from 1 to 6 pounds and standing 6 to 9 inches high, the Chihuahua (pronounced Chi-WAW-waw) is bred in two coat varieties: *Smooth* and *Long*, in many solid colors. His fine, arched body is supported on delicate legs. His rounded head tapers to a slim, pointed muzzle. His ears, set wide apart, are also pointed and are exceedingly large for a dog of this size. The Chihuahua was named after a state in Mexico, though experts say that he was not originally bred there. No one knows where he came from, but he has lived in the Western world for at least fifteen hundred years. The Mayans, a highly civilized Indian race that once occupied Central America, made stone carvings of this same little dog.

The Chihuahua has had both a luxurious and tragic history. A thousand years ago only the nobility could own him. Each tiny dog had a human slave to tend him. When the dog died, the slave was killed and buried with him. But when the dog's owner died, his tiny pet was slain so that in the spirit world he might guide his master to heaven. Perhaps the Mayans realized that the loyal little Chihuahua would rather die with his master than live without him. "Love me," his large, soft eyes seem to say, "and never, never leave me." It may be that it is this mute appeal that has made the Chihuahua a favorite among Toys.

But there are other reasons aside from appealing helplessness that have assured the popularity of Toy dogs. Apart from size, there is nothing helpless-looking about the *Pekingese*. Though only 6 to 9 inches high, weighing up to 14 pounds, the Peke views the world with imperial disdain. He has a right to do so, for his ancestors were the pampered darlings of China's royal court in the fabulous walled city of Peking. Here the Peke's long, straight coat with its thick mane was brushed by satin-robed attendants who fed him from gold dishes, ornamented with jewels. Even the color of the Peke's coat was once important, for it was thought that the colors of the newborn puppies foretold the fate of China for the coming year. The delicate hands of princesses stroked the Peke's broad forehead and twisted his long, raggedy ears. Empresses carried him in the wide sleeves of their embroidered gowns and undoubtedly laughed at his tiny, pushed-in, button-nosed face.

In the *Japanese Spaniel,* the disdain of the Pekingese becomes challenging scorn. He has been so long accustomed to reclining on silk cushions and being coddled by the aristocracy that he is positively arrogant. Slightly taller than the Pekingese, the Japanese Spaniel stands 10 inches high but weighs only from 6 to 9 pounds. His coat, more silky than the Peke's, is just as abundant. Usually white in color, it is touched with black, especially around the ears and the large, slightly protruding eyes. Though Japan claims him, he probably came from China, the gift of a Chinese emperor to a Japanese mikado.

It is believed that the *Pug* also came from China, brought by Dutch traders to the Western world in the sixteenth century. Some breeders of this dog say that it is wrong to call the Pug a Toy. They claim that he should be with Non-Sporting Dogs because he is taller (about 11 inches) and weighs more (from 14 to 18 pounds) than the average Toy. He is such a considerate, lovable companion that he has been called "the gentleman of dogs." His stocky, wide-chested body ends in a corkscrew tail over his back. His coat is short and glossy, silver-white or apricot-fawn. But it is always marked with black, particularly on the button or rose ears set on either side of a massive head. Black, too, is the blunt, square muzzle, and black shadows the Pug's large, dark, slightly protruding eyes. Deep lines mark his forehead, as though he were giving weighty attention to everything he observes.

Pug, Peke, and Japanese Spaniel are handsome but they are too independent to be cuddly. Yet each has his unique appeal. The woman who owns a Pug looks even more fragile and charming by contrast with this small, sturdy warrior. Pekes and Japanese Spaniels provide an air of noble arrogance which their owners may value. Add to this the fact that when these three dogs are with the ones they love, they become as playful as puppies, and their charm proves irresistible.

But what is the appeal of the *Affenpinscher* and the *Brussels Griffon?* There is nothing arrogant about them. They are not cute powder puffs like the Pomeranian. Neither do they possess the beauty of the Yorkshire's silken coat to recommend them.

Affenpinscher is German for "Monkey Terrier." Ten inches high, weighing 7 to 8 pounds, this monkey-faced dog is a small package of dynamite. His medium-short, rough coat, usually black, sprouts into a wild mop on top of his rounded head, produces moustaches on either side of his pointed muzzle, and shags down over his chest. He always looks as though he had just been battling a high wind. He has Terrier blood in him, and Terrier spirit, the I'll-die-before-I-give-up kind.

The Brussels Griffon has the same undaunted attitude. His short-haired, red-brown coat is rough textured and lies flatter than the Affenpinscher's except where it bursts into scraggly whiskers around his thrust-out chin. Small, perky ears are set wide apart on a broad forehead. Dark, almost popped eyes regard the world with a direct stare, behind which gleams a humorous twinkle. The history of the Brussels Griffon begins around the sixteenth century in Brussels, the capital of Belgium. There, street dogs made themselves useful by killing rats in the stables of carriage horses. It is thought that these dogs were crossed with the Affenpinscher to make them better ratters. Later, they were again crossed, this time with the Pug. In the process, the size of the dog dwindled to 8 to 10 inches and his weight to 7 to 12 pounds. The Brussels Griffon may be a coddled pet today, but he has inherited the intelligence of his ancestors, who had to earn their living by ratting, at the same time avoiding horses' nervous hooves. It may be that the Brussels Griffon remembers how his brother dogs were once considered street curs, to be kicked by irate humans, for this little dog is slow to give his friendship. When he does, he gives it with all his heart.

Some of the charm of the Affenpinscher and the Brussels Griffon lies in their quaint ugliness. But most of it is in their attitude toward life. They are afraid of nothing and can turn into small furies when danger threatens. At times, these minute dogs march around with enormous seriousness. At others, they are comics, seeming to laugh at the world as well as at themselves. They not only amuse, but by example they give new hope and courage to their owners, along with their devotion.

Occasionally, reducing the size of a dog accents one part of him until it is out of proportion to the rest, as with the very long coat of the Yorkshire Terrier. This

AFFENPINSCHER

BRUSSELS GRIFFON

PUG

ITALIAN GREYHOUND

contrast cannot be found in the miniature *Italian Greyhound*, the *Miniature Pinscher*, or the *Toy Manchester Terrier*. These three dogs are elegantly formed.

The Miniature Pinscher resembles a Doberman Pinscher reduced to 10 to 12 inches in height and from 6 to 10 pounds in weight. His glossy coat can be black with rust-red or tan markings, dark brown with red or yellow markings, or a deep red. His erect, pointed ears are cropped, as is his tail.

The Toy Manchester Terrier is practically the mirror image of the Standard Manchester except for size. The Toy variety weighs 5 to 12 pounds. Its full, tip-pointed ears stand up, while the ears of the larger Standard variety may tip forward. The Toy wears the same smooth black coat touched with mahogany red.

These two small dogs have a lineage that goes back several centuries, but the Italian Greyhound can trace his for more than two thousand years. Before Julius Caesar ruled Rome, the Italian Greyhound was pacing beside lovely ladies in their villa gardens. Even then, this dog, 10 inches in height and weighing about 8 pounds, had the same arched grace of body and the flowing lines of the big Greyhound. Elegant is the word to describe him, as it is for the Miniature Pinscher and the Toy Manchester. Another Toy is the *Silky Terrier,* a cross between Australian and Yorkshire Terriers. It has a long, flat, silky, blue coat with tan markings. It stands 9 to 10 inches tall and weighs 8 to 10 pounds. Though a Toy, he is credited with protecting poultry from rats and snakes. The latest breed admitted to the Toy group is the *Shih Tzu,* an oriental cross between the Lhasa Apso and the Pekingese.

Cavalier King Charles Spaniels, Miniature Bull Terriers, and *Spinoni Italiani* are in the process of qualifying for registration in the AKC Toy group.

It is amazing how sturdy these Toys are. Even the fragile-appearing Chihuahua does not need to be carried around on a pillow, though he loves to be pampered. All Toys do; they insist upon it. They are so attached to people that they prefer them to dogs, including their own kind. And they exhibit every trick they know, from forlorn helplessness to comical antics, to gain and hold attention.

All these dogs have been bred from larger dogs, some so large that they are hard to control. The fighting spirit of an Affenpinscher would be dangerous in a big dog. In the Toy, it is amusing. A sled dog cannot be cuddled like a Pomeranian. A Greyhound is too big to be picked up, but the tiny Italian Greyhound just fits in one's arms. Self-sufficient dogs can be wonderful companions but they cannot be carried or cared for like a baby. They do not demand the constant attention that may help to fill otherwise lonely lives. That is the task of the Toys. It is a big task, far out of proportion to their size. In performing it, they are still serving man, holding a very definite place in human lives. Though Toys depend upon people, people depend as much, if not more, upon Toys. This is because in both humans and dogs there is a perpetual yearning to be needed, to be wanted— and to be loved.

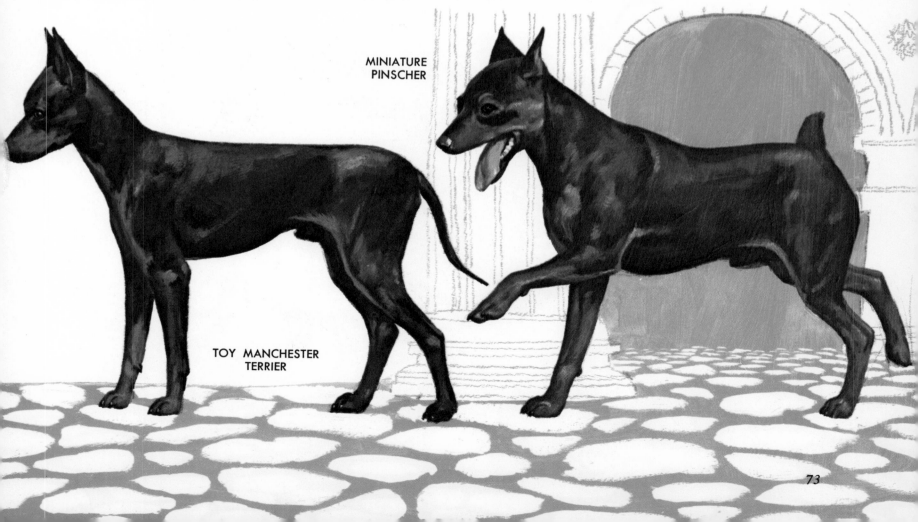

MINIATURE PINSCHER

TOY MANCHESTER TERRIER

non-sporting dogs

NON-SPORTING DOGS are really companion dogs. And in that word "companion" lies the strangest and most wonderful of all the true stories that throughout history have been told about dogs and men.

When the great elk, the boars, the wolves, and other predators had been killed off or forced by advancing civilization to retreat to the wildest parts of the world, dogs were no longer necessary. They had performed their duty. They had saved man from suffering and hardship. They might have gone the way of the animals they once fought. But they did not. Today, there are more dogs in the world than there were when they were vitally needed.

The reason is that a dog gave to man something more than just his usefulness. He gave man understanding and companionship. Often this part of the dog's personality was not revealed until his usefulness was at an end. The *Bulldog,* so English that he is often used as a symbol of the nation, has a fierce, terrible, fighting history.

A black page in the record of man and dog began around the year 1200 in the reign of King John. A noble Lord of Stamford, pacing his castle halls, saw two bulls fighting. Suddenly the butcher's dogs came rushing in and chased one angry bull through the town. This so amused His Lordship that he set aside the meadow in which the bulls had been fighting for what was then known as "bull-baiting." This means that dogs once used to drive cattle to market were set upon a bull until dogs or bull, or both, were brought down.

Some of these cattle dogs were not ferocious enough for this terrible sport. So men began to breed dogs for endurance, courage, and fortitude. The breeders were not interested in how the dog looked but in his ability to hang on to a bull. For that reason, the Bulldog has an undershot jaw so strong that when once it has clamped onto his foe, it can be pried loose only with great difficulty. His nose is pressed back into his face. This enabled him to breathe while he was clinging to the bull, even as the maddened animal shook him back and forth in the air. The dog's great shoulders and widely spaced forelegs—necessary to resist sidewise thrust—give him an almost squared arch in the front part of his body. The muscles across his shoulders took the brunt of the bull's savage shaking as he tried to dislodge the tormenting dog.

BULLDOG

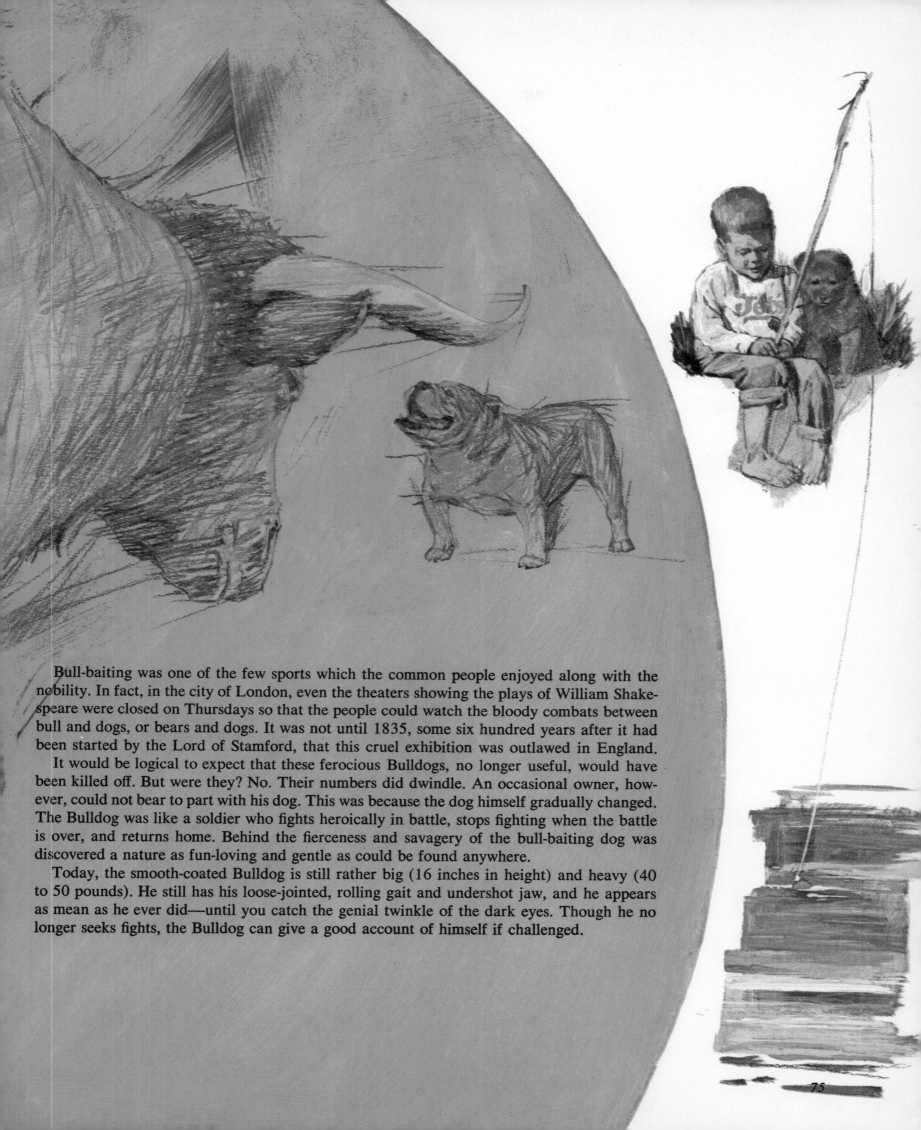

Bull-baiting was one of the few sports which the common people enjoyed along with the nobility. In fact, in the city of London, even the theaters showing the plays of William Shakespeare were closed on Thursdays so that the people could watch the bloody combats between bull and dogs, or bears and dogs. It was not until 1835, some six hundred years after it had been started by the Lord of Stamford, that this cruel exhibition was outlawed in England.

It would be logical to expect that these ferocious Bulldogs, no longer useful, would have been killed off. But were they? No. Their numbers did dwindle. An occasional owner, however, could not bear to part with his dog. This was because the dog himself gradually changed. The Bulldog was like a soldier who fights heroically in battle, stops fighting when the battle is over, and returns home. Behind the fierceness and savagery of the bull-baiting dog was discovered a nature as fun-loving and gentle as could be found anywhere.

Today, the smooth-coated Bulldog is still rather big (16 inches in height) and heavy (40 to 50 pounds). He still has his loose-jointed, rolling gait and undershot jaw, and he appears as mean as he ever did—until you catch the genial twinkle of the dark eyes. Though he no longer seeks fights, the Bulldog can give a good account of himself if challenged.

About a hundred years ago, there were Toy Bulldogs in England. They did not prove popular. Some experts say that these toys were shipped to France. Here breeders crossed them with small, pug-faced dogs from the Mediterranean. The result was the *French Bulldog*. He has the undershot jaw and pushed-in nose of the English dog. He does not, however, have the heavy jowls, nor do his lower teeth thrust out beyond his upper lip. His tail is short and tapered. His ears, like those of a bat, stand straight up rather than flop over. However, he has the same courage, the same adventurous spirit as the Bulldog. The French Bulldog is only 10 to 14 inches tall and 19 to 28 pounds in weight. He wears a short-haired coat, easy to keep clean, of grayish black or brownish yellow.

The small French dog is a favorite of the city dweller. Whatever traits he has inherited from his fighting ancestors have been long overcome in his desire to be a companion to his master and his master's family.

The large heart of the small *Boston Terrier* is also given wholly to his human companions. He, too, has forgotten his fighting past, for his ancestors were Bull Terriers, bred to fight other dogs in pits for the amusement of those who did not think of dogs as valued living creatures.

There is more Terrier in the Boston than Bull. His short, square, wide and deep muzzle covers his underjaw. His

FRENCH BULLDOG

ears come more to a point but are just as alert as those of the French Bulldog. He has the same short tail. His eyes, ears, and most of his trim, strong body are either black or red-brown. His short, smooth coat shines like satin. This, with his white muzzle and the white blaze running down his forehead, collar, chest, and forelegs, gives him an elegant, dressed-up appearance whenever he walks in the city parks.

The small aristocrat (height 14 to 15 inches, weight 12 to 25 pounds) is the all-American breed. It made its appearance in Boston, and it is from this city that he takes his name. It is from the Bostonians that he takes his disposition, also. He has beautiful manners. But, like all gentlemen, the Boston Terrier when confronted by danger will not run away.

The wonder of all companion dogs is that they have sensed in people the desire for something more than

BOSTON TERRIER

food, clothing, and shelter. Instinct tells them that the human need of friendship, loyalty, and kindness is perhaps even greater than the need for aids to survival. The remarkable fact is that these dogs have seemingly ignored the original purpose for which they were bred and have developed another side of their natures.

Such a dog is the *Chow Chow* (or Chow). He comes from China. In fact, he is so Oriental that he has the almond-shaped eyes of the Chinese. Standing 18 to 20 inches at the shoulder and weighing 40 to 65 pounds, he has an abundant, off-standing coat. A bushy tail arches over his back, and he wears a great lion's mane as a ruff around his neck. His muzzle is medium short and broad. His ears are so small they are almost lost in his dense fur. One feature that sets him apart from any other dog is the blue-black color of his tongue. It looks as though he has been eating blueberries.

When the early ships of the Western world sailed into Chinese harbors, some of these dogs were sold to the captain and crew along with jade, carved ivory, bronze figures, and exquisite Chinese porcelain. The master of the vessels listed all of these various items under the heading of "chowchow." This was pidgin English for all types of bric-a-brac from the Orient. So this dog became known in Europe and America as the Chow Chow. But ask for him by that name in China and you will not be understood. There he is called the bear dog, the wolf dog, or the black-tongued dog.

In the Orient, records of the Chow Chow go back over two thousand years. Some people argue that this breed may even have been the ancestor of the Samoyed and the Norwegian Elkhound.

During his long career, the Chow Chow has been asked to do almost everything a dog can do. He has herded, guarded, hunted. He has tracked bear, deer, tigers in Siberia and, undoubtedly, wild horses. He has played the part of a Setter, a Pointer, and a Retriever. In Mongolia, he was expert in the hunting of pheasants. He has pulled sleds or had packs hung over his back. Often he sacrificed his life that the Chinese might be fed, for he was used as meat for the table.

His shape and disposition are the same today as they were thousands of years ago. He is just as capable of hunting the Siberian Tiger or drawing a sled as he was then. He is reserved toward strangers but his history reveals the reason. From the way he has been treated, one wonders how he can endure people at all —how he can still give his master and his master's family the same complete loyalty.

The *Keeshond,* national dog of Holland, has the

CHOW CHOW

79

KEESHOND

same arctic ancestors as the Chow Chow. During his journey to Holland, however, his appearance was somewhat changed. While he kept the bushy tail curled over his back, the dense, harsh coat, and the ruff around his neck, his muzzle became longer than the Chow Chow's and also more pointed. This, with his alert, stand-up ears and merry, twinkling eyes, gives one the impression of a fox's head coming out of a fox-fur collar. The ample coat of the Keeshond reaches only to his legs, where it is shorter. His double coat, like that of all Northern dogs, has two colors. The undercoat may be pearl-gray or cream. The outer, a mixture of gray and black, stands away from the body, giving him his furry look. He is easily groomed—in fact, the less groomed he is, the better he looks.

Dogs have been involved in many of man's battles. The Keeshond breed nearly came to an end in Holland's political revolution, a few years before the French revolution. Kees de Gyselaer, leader of the middle-class Patriots, loved his little barge dog so much that he gave it his name, Kees. (*Hond,* in Dutch, means dog.) The dog became the symbol, the mascot of the Patriots. When the Prince of Orange's upper-class party defeated the Patriots, it was as much as a man's life was worth for him to own a Keeshond. Many of these dogs were put to death that their presence might not betray the fact that their masters had been Patriots.

A century and a half later, a Baroness searched river boats, farms, and trucks in Holland for specimens of the almost extinct breed, and she was able to reestablish it.

The Keeshond, living for hundreds of years in a land of great dikes and where every inch of earth is cultivated, has never learned to hunt. He has served as a guard in the homes and on the canal barges that brought the flowers and produce to market, and as a family companion.

When the hunting and fighting dogs sleep, undoubtedly they dream of flushing birds or tracking elk or being pitted against the bull or the bear, for they twitch and snuffle and give small, excited whimpers. But when the Keeshond dozes by the fire, his dreams are almost certainly those of watchful guarding of the lives and property of his master and family. They are his world, and his one desire is to please.

Holland is not the only Northern European country with canals. Belgium, next to Holland, has waterways, too. Here the barges are guarded by the *Schipperke*. In Flemish, this name means "little captain" (from *schipper,* "captain," plus the diminutive *ke).*

Guarding the produce on trucks or barges, however, was not the little dog's only duty during these hundreds of years. Horses moved the barges up and down the stream by big ropes. The burden was heavy and the horses would naturally stop whenever they could. Then the Schipperke would bark at them and run forward as though to attack them. This would force the horses to move on.

Where there is water, there is always the problem of rats, and these the Schipperke fought with the same, quick intelligence that he showed in guarding his master's property.

Alertness is still in every line of his body from his stand-up, or pricked, ears to his little stub of a tail (if he has one—some are born tailless). His pointed muzzle is as curious as that of a fox, which he resembles. His dark, almond-shaped eyes miss nothing that happens around him. About 13 inches in height, part of his 12-to-18-pound weight is in his thick, dense, double coat. This is fairly short and stand-off, except for the extra thickness around head and down chest and forelegs which gives him added protection against the dampness and chilling mists that come up from the waters.

Those who have owned a Schipperke call him the best of all house dogs. He is neat and clean. He is also daring and merry. It is almost impossible to be dull or depressed when a Schip is around.

SCHIPPERKE

Where the Schipperke's known history goes back hundreds of years, the *Dalmatian* may have posed for Greek sculptors sixteen hundred years before the birth of Christ. Some people even believe that this dog came originally from Bengal, in India, where he was known as the Bengal Harrier, or hunter of hares. The Dalmatian traveled with the Romany gypsies. Like the gypsies, this dog has been in so many countries that he can call none of them his home. His name comes from Dalmatia, on the eastern shore of the Gulf of Venice.

In his wanderings, the Dalmatian has done many kinds of work. He has acted as sentinel on the borders of countries and guarded personal property. He has herded sheep. He has killed rats, hunted hares, run in packs on the trail of stag and boar, and flushed wildfowl and retrieved them.

Today, he is best known as a coaching dog. Comparatively large, some 23 inches in height and weighing from 35 to 55 pounds, this clean-cut, sleek white dog with his dark, dime-to-half-dollar-size spots, had a gait which was perfect for this work. He had the rhythmic pacing of a fine horse, and was at least as tireless.

Originally, his duties may have been to guard the coach. Actually, his popularity lay in the fact that he gave distinction to the vehicle, an impression that the people within it were aristocrats. This dog could follow beside the rear wheels, between them, or under the coach itself, the last a very dangerous position had he not moved in such perfect harmony with the coach that he seemed a part of it.

When fire engines were drawn by horses in the United States, the Dalmatian was the chosen dog to race with men and horses to the conflagration. Because he also guarded the firehouses and served as mascot to the brigade, he has remained long after the old fire horses were put out to pasture.

This lithe, spotted dog can vary his disposition with the swiftness of a quick-change artist. If called upon, he can be the stern, alert sentinel or the jaunty companion of purebred hunting horses. Or he can act like a clown. In the home, on the stage, or in the circus, he matches the standard-sized *Poodle* for the ease with which he learns his tricks.

DALMATIAN

MINIATURE POODLE

The Poodle is the Cinderella of the canine family. He was first just a plain water dog, probably used as a retriever of water fowl. But even before the first century A.D., his long coat, that had a tendency to twist into cords, so weighted him down that he had to be clipped. It was discovered that unless some hair was left around the upper part of his body, he caught cold in the water. He needed hair around his joints, also, to prevent rheumatism in them.

The rough coat of the Standard Poodle reveals a clear resemblance to the coat of the Portuguese Water Dog, companion of the fishermen of Portugal. But the trimming of the playful Poodle gives him a clownish appearance. The traveling carnival people were quick to notice how the audiences laughed at the antics of a clipped Poodle. At first these performers may have taken the dog with them just for his looks. They soon found, however, that an almost human intelligence lay behind that sharp-nosed face. Here was a dog that could be taught to do almost anything on a stage from jumping through hoops to shooting off small cannon in mimic war.

For a time the upper classes laughed at the Poodle's clowning but had nothing to do with the dog himself. Gradually, however, they realized that this very stage training proved how smart he was. From the time of Louis XVI of France, the Poodle has risen in popularity in nearly every country in the Western world. Americans breed Poodles in three varieties, identical except for size: *Standard,* over 15 inches tall, 20 to 50 pounds; *Miniature,* 10 to 15 inches, about 16 pounds; *Toy,* not over 10 inches, under 10 pounds. France has claimed the Poodle as her national dog. But the English word Poodle must come from the German *pudel,* and some authorities claim this is the country of his origin.

Probably only those who know the history of the Poodle realize that he also hunted truffles. This delicious fungus grows underground, and it takes a dog to scent it out. Today, in some parts of the world, truffle dogs earn enough money for their masters to keep a large family comfortably. These dogs are Poodles crossed with Terriers. About all that is left of the Poodle blood in them is the sharp-pointed nose and the droopy ears. The rest is that of a strong-bodied, short-coated Terrier.

The Poodle is now a member of society, with his own beauty salon, and an elegant summer and winter wardrobe which he occasionally deigns to model for fashion magazines. He may be white, cream, blue, gray, silver, rich brown, a milk-coffee shade, or apricot—all solid colors. Yet the Standard Poodle, for all his elegance, can still hunt with the best of the Retrievers, and pull a duck out of the water. That he prefers to be a companion is simply because he has reached the point where he considers himself a person. He prefers

TOY POODLE

STANDARD POODLE

people to his own kind. They are probably more amusing. Poodles are by far the most popular breed in this country at this time.

While the Poodle has been associated with humans for over two thousand years, no one knows how long the *Lhasa Apso* has been guarding the homes of his masters in the villages around Lhasa, capital of Tibet.

This dog was not given its name until it arrived in the West. In his homeland, he is known as *Abso Seng Kye,* which means "Bark Lion Sentinel Dog." Certainly, this little dog has the keenness of hearing which makes him a perfect guard, and the courage of a lion—even though that courage is stuffed into a body only 9 to 11 inches tall, weighing around 15 pounds.

In appearance, he looks like a small edition of the Old English Sheepdog, except for his tail, which, like all Northern dogs' tails, curls over his back. His shaggy coat is dense and hard, to give him greater protection against the high mountain cold. In Tibet, because he has been given the name of a lion, tawny, lionlike colors are preferred, though he does come in smoke-gray, slate-blue, white, brown, or black.

LHASA APSO

A native to Tibet, and a beautiful toy dog, is the *Tibetan Spaniel*. There is also the grandfather of all Mastiffs, the great, powerful, shaggy *Tibetan Mastiff*. But it is the Lhasa Apso which has always been most loved, not only because he was charmingly affectionate —to those who were kind to him—but because by his presence he gave to his owners such a sense of security. The giant, savage Mastiff chained outside the walls could be poisoned. The thief could get into the courtyard. But he could not enter the house without every person in it being aroused by the barking of the Sentinel Dog. This small creature was held in such high esteem that his owners would not think of selling him. Occasionally, he was sent as a gift to the ruler of China or given to one of the few foreigners permitted to enter China.

It was as a gift that a pair of Lhasa Apsos came to the Western world. Today, the Lhasa Apso, resembling a walking dishmop, is performing the same service of charming and guarding in homes over Europe and America. He takes his duty seriously, and his owners have found him to be better than a burglar alarm.

Non-sporting dogs have come from all over the world—from the soaring mountains of Tibet, from the beautiful coast of the Mediterranean. They have climbed out of the water where they once retrieved wildfowl. They have forsaken the chase after deer and boars, and have stopped flushing birds. They have left behind them the pits where they battled other dogs, in order to be gentle, loyal companions to humans.

In this new role, all kinds of dogs are beginning to play a part. One of their most recent projects is giving their understanding and devotion to wayward boys. At one school for delinquents, three dogs are placed in each cottage. Into their ears the boys pour troubles that they might not feel free to tell the adults around them. And in caring for the dogs, they forget themselves. As one boy has said, "It's nice to have someone around besides people."

your dog

DOG BREEDERS throughout the world agree on one point: When you purchase a dog, you are adding a new member to your family. This new member is a unique personality. You must consider his happiness, and the happiness of the people around you, as well as your own. If the dog fails to win the love of your family, or if he is unfriendly toward your neighbors, owning him may result in a series of quarrels and heartaches. Before looking for a particular dog, you should ask yourself several questions.

First, how much chance do you want to take about how the puppy will turn out when he grows up? Puppies of mixed or unknown ancestry—called *mongrels*—may be cute and appealing, and they may grow up to be entirely satisfactory, but when they are young it is guesswork how large they will grow or what kind of coat or temperament will mature. And if they are ever to have puppies of their own, the gamble continues into the next generation. The idea that mongrels are the smartest dogs has never been proved, for there are no accurate comparisons. Usually the smartest teacher turns out the smartest dog. *Pedigreed* puppies are those whose ancestors have been written down by generations, according to breeds they most resembled. You gamble less in acquiring one of these.

The ancestors of *purebred* puppies have been carefully limited to a single breed, and their pedigrees have been registered by the American Kennel Club in order to insure accuracy. Pure breeds of dogs have been described and illustrated in Chapters Two to Seven of this book. When you buy a puppy from a registered litter, you know that he will grow up within the comparatively slight variations accepted within that breed. A woolly Afghan puppy, for example, will develop the long, silky Afghan coat and aristocratic expression, whereas a similarly woolly German Shepherd puppy will grow up to have the coat and contours of that breed. It is only with respect to purebred puppies that it is possible to exercise much forethought in selection. When you consider that the puppy you choose will probably live with you up to a dozen years, a few dollars difference in original cost is spread over more than a hundred months. A purebred puppy may well be worth it.

Next, have you a definite purpose in mind for the dog? Is he to go hunting during the season? Is he to act as guardian of property or people? Or is companionship the main reason for adding him to the family?

If a hunting breed is desired, the hunter in the family will probably have contacts with hunter friends through whom suitable puppies can usually be located. For guarding extensive premises, the larger working breeds are appropriate, and they readily respond to training. In smaller areas, like apartments, smaller breeds can raise an alarm, and sounds of their presence discourage intruders. But don't let too much false-alarm barking disturb the neighbors.

If the dog is to be a companion, you will have to decide whether he will live indoors or out. Do you live in a cold climate where a long coat is a comfort in winter, or in a hot climate where it is a discomfort in summer? Have you a roomy house and money for proper feeding of a large dog? Will it have plenty of exercise, or would a smaller, shorter-legged breed better suit family conditions? Will someone have time to care for a fancy coat, such as that of a Poodle, or is a carefree short coat more appropriate? And as to ages, young puppies of the smallest or largest breeds are not practical with very young children. The best intentioned youngsters can hurt a Toy dog, and the best intentioned Boxer puppy can knock over a fairly good-sized boy. And a dog the size of an adult Great Dane can sweep a table clear with one enthusiastic wag of its tail!

Another question before you look for an individual dog: Should you buy a male or female? Years ago, male dogs were preferred by almost everyone except dog breeders. More recently, it has become widely recognized that females—which are called *bitches* by breeders—are practical in city or suburb, where they will not be allowed to roam. In general, females are gentler and more responsive to children. And they do not seek to relieve themselves as often or as extensively. Twice a year, they will be in heat for about three weeks. During that time they must be kept from contact with other dogs, unless you plan to have a litter of puppies. If it is inconvenient for you to protect your female dog at these times, your veterinarian will board her for you.

Then there are the characteristic temperaments of each breed. Long observation has classified Spaniels and Beagles as gentle, German Shepherds as receptive to training, Terriers as excitable, and Poodles as adaptable to a wide range of environment. On the whole, dogs are probably the most conformable of animals because they have lived closer to people than have other species. Within each breed, even within most individuals, there is a desire to please.

When you have settled on a breed, you can seek a kennel in the classified section of the telephone directory or in the classified columns of your local newspaper, or you can write to the American Kennel Club* for names of breeders of that breed and the name of the secretary of the parent breed club, who can supply more names. At the same time, ask for a show calendar, the secretary of the nearest all-breed show-giving club, and the booklet of registration rules. By attending a show, you can see good examples of all but the rarest breeds, and you can make contacts with breeders of typical puppies. A pet shop may have a puppy to suit you, or be able to help you to learn of a kennel that has.

The next step is to select your dog. In many respects it is well to be guided by first impressions. If the premises are clean and well cared for, so probably has been the puppy you will inspect. At a breeder's, you should be able to see the puppy's mother, and perhaps the father and some adult relatives. These are the best guide to what you may expect when your puppy grows up. As to health, a cold nose is usually a sign of no fever. Check also for hearing. His eyes should be clear and without discharge, and his skin should be free from rash or blemishes. Enlarged or tender wrists may be a sign of rickets. His body should be rounded but not bloated. After these preliminaries, the final choice should be based upon mutual attraction. Hold out your hand and call him. Should he come to you eagerly, let that decide.

Now some paper work. You should obtain a bill of sale, which is subject to a health inspection by your own veterinarian within forty-eight hours. You should also ask for his registration certificate or the blue form identifying your puppy as one of a registered litter, which permits you to register the puppy at your convenience so that he can compete in events under AKC rules and produce puppies eligible for registration. If you are not buying from the breeder, you should receive a gray intermediate form. Note the dates of each vaccination

*51 Madison Avenue, New York, New York 10010

injection, and also whether vaccine or serum was administered, so that your veterinarian can complete the protection against puppy diseases. Also jot down what food the puppy is getting, and at what hours. Continuing this schedule is the best insurance against digestive upsets. You can make gradual changes after the puppy feels at home. Ask what exercise he needs, how to keep him brushed and clean, and how to keep his toenails short.

A temporary bed can be made of a corrugated carton. It should be long enough for the puppy to stretch out, with sides and back at least a foot high, and a three-inch front to protect against drafts. It should be lined with easily washable material like old terry-cloth towels, and it should contain something to keep him warm. (He may take to your old sweater and associate your scent with you and his new home.) This bed can be replaced as the puppy outgrows it, and, ultimately, you can provide a more formal bed. If the dog is to live outdoors, put the bed in a doghouse to protect against inclement weather.

The first times the dog travels by car, take newspapers in case he should become carsick. Never allow the dog to put his head out of an open window. Wind, along with dust, may injure the dog's eyes or ears. Never leave a dog in a car without window-top ventilation or where it might be exposed to continuous sunshine.

Once at home, persuade him to accept his bed by showing him it belongs to him. His instinct will operate against soiling the bed. A puppy is like a baby. At the start of housebreaking, he has little or no awareness of bodily functions, but with firmness, patience, and kindness he will learn quickly what he is expected to do. Put the bed in a bathroom or playroom with a waterproof floor, and cover the rest of the floor with newspapers. When he has used the paper, praise him; then he can be released to other parts of the house for a short time before being returned to his bed. As he grows older, the times between elimination become longer, and the newspaper can be reduced to several layers of a double page. Always expect him to need his bathroom first thing in the morning, last thing before bedtime, right after each meal, and after a nap. If you have a fenced yard, put him out at corresponding times, or if he goes to the door. Let him in only after you know that he has relieved himself.

A dog is a carnivore—his digestion is adapted to more meat than ours and he cannot digest raw starches. Proper diet for a grown dog should include about thirty percent meat, thirty percent well-cooked carbohydrates, preferably whole-grain products, ten to fifteen percent fat, and the remaining twenty-five percent green vegetables, which should be finely shredded. There are good canned and kibbled dog foods on the market; the latter, fed dry, helps keep the teeth clean. So-called complete

foods—maintenance diets for comparatively inactive adult dogs—can be supplemented by the addition of a little meat, a spoonful of dry skimmed milk, and some fat during the first year for small breeds, and for larger breeds until fully grown. Cottage cheese can replace part of the meat, as can lean table scraps. Variety is good. A daily multivitamin and mineral pill or concentrate will probably provide a better source of vitamins than a combination of vegetables. Watch the dog's condition and regulate the amount you feed in order to maintain the proper weight for size of frame. Avoid fried food, seasonings, and highly spiced sauces. Limit occasional candy to pieces no larger than a peanut. A spoonful of ice cream never hurt a healthy dog. Fresh water in a clean dish should always be available.

Puppies two to four months old should be fed three times a day; the food should be between room and body temperatures. Then, until fully grown, the dog should be fed twice a day. After that, if he shares the family living quarters, it is considerate to divide the dog's food into morning and evening meals, more or less when the family eats, although you and the dog should not share the dining room at mealtime. Adult outdoor dogs thrive on one meal late in the day. Feeding dishes of long-eared breeds should be narrow enough for the ears to hang outside. Pick up and wash dishes promptly after a meal. Stainless steel is the easiest to care for.

Dogs love gnawing on bones. This activity helps to cut their second teeth, at four to six months, and to keep the teeth clean all their lives. Bones should be big and solid. A splinter from a large bone—or from those in pork or lamb chops, chicken, or fish—may be-

come stuck in a dog's throat and choke him to death. There are nylon or rawhide "chew toys" which reduce the temptation to chew the wrong things.

Meanwhile, you will have taken your dog to the veterinarian to complete his vaccination. Let the veterinarian check for worms and for skin condition, and ask him to tell you the best way to keep him free from fleas, ticks, and lice. A record of your dog will be kept, and whenever he refuses two meals or appears sluggish you can telephone to see what attention he requires. A dog's normal temperature is about 101°F. by rectal thermometer.

If you hope to train your dog to be friendly, confident, and yet obedient, be sure that he knows what to expect from you. Stop him the first time he jumps on a couch or chair that you don't wish him on—and stop him *every* time he tries it after that, not just sometimes. Then you are being fair to him. He'll know.

If you must punish him, *do it at once*. If you wait a few minutes he will have forgotten what he did and have no idea of the reason for the punishment. A rolled newspaper kept handy makes enough noise when used to strike his rear end, the furniture he is tempted to jump on, or the floor near an "accident" to reinforce the disciplinary message. Reserve your hand for the rare, instant emergency spanks on the appropriate place; never strike a dog's face, either with paper or with your hand, lest you injure his eyes. Let him know firmly

but not angrily exactly what he has done wrong—*then show him what he should do*. Praise him when he does it. Patience and praise work better than threats, for a dog craves approval. He will put forth his best efforts to gain it.

When you first take your dog for a walk, use a firm buckled collar, adjusted so that he cannot pull out of it, and a strong leash not more than six feet long. Talk to him as you would to a person. He cannot understand your words, but he'll know your voice is friendly, and, if you are consistent, he will gradually associate the sounds with what you mean. If he follows you at once, you are lucky. He usually has to be coaxed. A series of light twitches on the lead often gets him started.

If he lies down, don't drag him. Don't enter into a contest which will build up his resistance. He soon will tire of hanging back, and then he will enjoy such walks with you for the rest of his life. Do not be impatient when he stops to sniff at trees or bushes. He has caught the scent of another animal. He "reads" with his nose, the way your eyes scan a picture or read a page. Never let him off the leash where there may be automobile traffic—he needs only one dash into the street for you to have a dead or badly injured puppy. The first time you expect him to eliminate on such an exercise trip, have patience, for the leash and outdoor sights, sounds, and smells distract him. Do not let him soil the sidewalk or a neighbor's yard.

From the beginning, a puppy should learn simple basic commands: *come,* easiest taught at mealtime; *down,* with the aid of a firm push, to which it is helpful to add *stay* and a threatening gesture; *off,* when he is tempted to jump on forbidden furniture; *quiet,* to stop barking; and *no* or *stop* in a severe voice to interrupt anything he is doing. During training, *never lose your temper.* Remember how you felt when you were shouted at or slapped for not immediately understanding what was expected of you.

More formal obedience training should not be expected before six months; even then, lessons in *heeling, sitting,* and *staying* while you walk away should not last more than five minutes, although they can be repeated several times a day. As he gets older, training sessions can be lengthened. There are many good books on training at stores or libraries that will help you. Or you can take your dog to an obedience school to learn lessons with other dogs. Tidbits are not allowed in formal obedience exercises; what your dog wants most is your approval.

By this time, if you bought a purebred puppy and have taken good care of him, he probably has been admired by many people. You are proud of him and you may be thinking of showing him in competition for ribbons and trophies when he passes the minimum age of six months. The dog show is an established and honored event. Your dog will probably be as thrilled as you are. Most dogs love to show off in the ring.

The first dog shows were held in England over one hundred years ago. They were designed more as sales displays than as competitions to honor quality. Early exhibitors were required to put a selling price on each dog, and owners like the Queen of England and the Czar of Russia set prohibitive prices as high as $50,000 to be sure their entries were not claimed. Dog shows have been held in this country since 1877, when 1,177 dogs were entered at Gilmore's Garden, New York, for four days. It is a coincidence that the offices of the American Kennel Club are now located in a building on the same piece of land. Nowadays only a few of the largest winter shows continue for as long as two days; most are one-day outdoor events on turf, with tents for possible wet weather. Here dog owners and the dog-loving public can compare, and delight in, the beauty, grooming, personality, and performance of representative examples of the various breeds.

The American Kennel Club has set up rules for dog shows, which will be sent to you on request. In many localities, there are dog clubs—some for one particular breed, some for the purpose of holding all-breed dog shows. Probably such a club holds match shows, less formal training operations at which puppies and novice exhibitors can practice. At such a match you also can learn what preparations your puppy may need, besides

training, to make a favorable show debut. Here you can also learn about obedience competition and training.

The show calendar mentioned above will give you the dates and the superintendent's or show secretary's name for the dog shows near you. At least six weeks before a show date, write the superintendent or the show secretary for a premium list and entry blank, which you fill out from information on your dog's registration certificate. (If you have only its blue certificate of litter registration, a dog can be shown three times using its litter number.) The closing date for entries will be stated, and it is strictly enforced, so mail your blank and entry fee in plenty of time. A few days before the show, you will receive an identification card and ticket, which will admit you and your dog, and a program stating at what time and in which ring your breed will be judged. Be at the ring gate early to get your identifying armband and watch earlier exhibitors go through their paces.

The judge, who has served an apprenticeship and whose qualifications have been approved by the AKC, will watch the dogs, led by their owners or handlers, enter the ring; will examine and evaluate each dog's type and conformation as he stands in show pose, with head, ears, and tail in proper position for his breed; will note his temperament; will test his gait; and will compare the entries standing and trotting, using the Standard of Perfection for that breed as a gauge. Ribbons are awarded in each class in order of merit: blue, red, yellow, and white. One purple ribbon in each sex is awarded, with points toward championship, and a purple and gold ribbon goes to the Best of Breed. A red, white, and blue rosette is given to the dog judged Best in Show. In breed judging, the steward will tell you if your dog is needed for further judging.

Many shows have junior showmanship classes for boys and girls 10 to 16 years old, where they can compete for awards based on their skill in handling dogs.

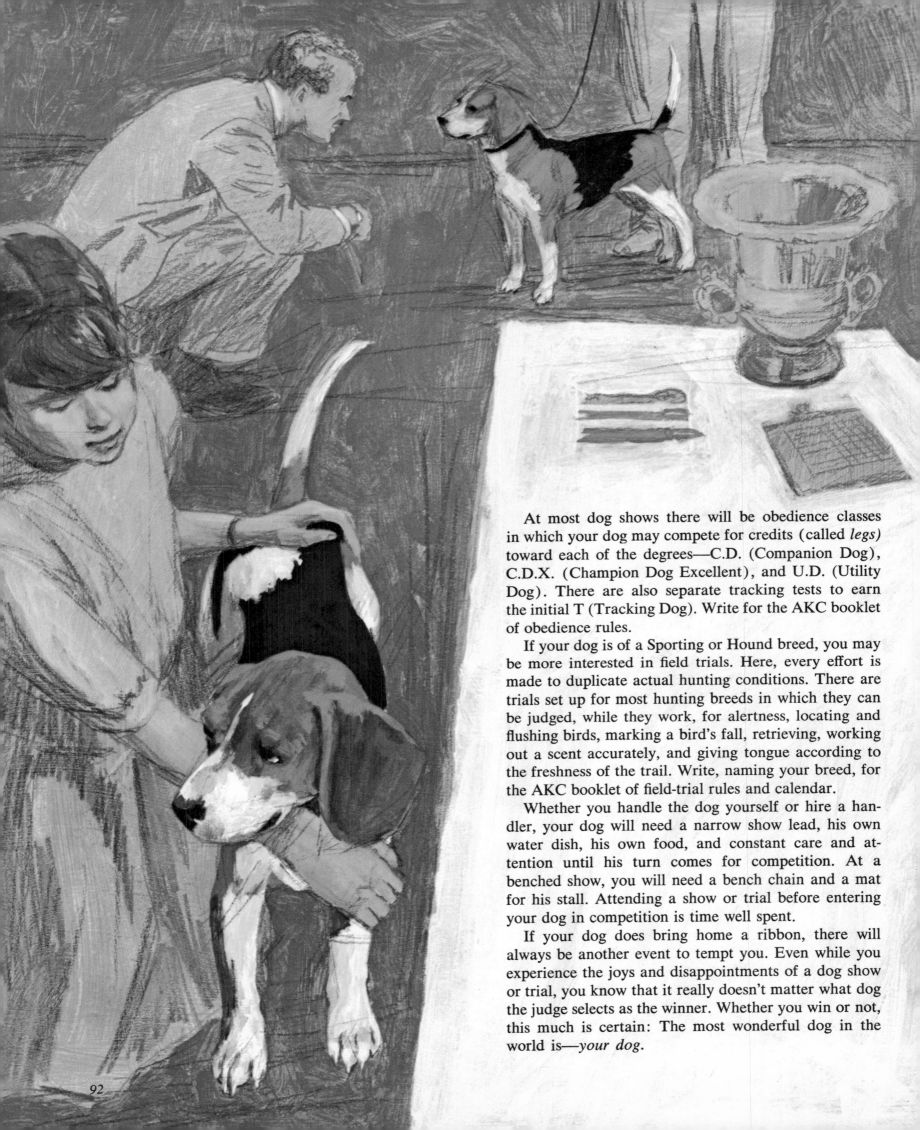

At most dog shows there will be obedience classes in which your dog may compete for credits (called *legs*) toward each of the degrees—C.D. (Companion Dog), C.D.X. (Champion Dog Excellent), and U.D. (Utility Dog). There are also separate tracking tests to earn the initial T (Tracking Dog). Write for the AKC booklet of obedience rules.

If your dog is of a Sporting or Hound breed, you may be more interested in field trials. Here, every effort is made to duplicate actual hunting conditions. There are trials set up for most hunting breeds in which they can be judged, while they work, for alertness, locating and flushing birds, marking a bird's fall, retrieving, working out a scent accurately, and giving tongue according to the freshness of the trail. Write, naming your breed, for the AKC booklet of field-trial rules and calendar.

Whether you handle the dog yourself or hire a handler, your dog will need a narrow show lead, his own water dish, his own food, and constant care and attention until his turn comes for competition. At a benched show, you will need a bench chain and a mat for his stall. Attending a show or trial before entering your dog in competition is time well spent.

If your dog does bring home a ribbon, there will always be another event to tempt you. Even while you experience the joys and disappointments of a dog show or trial, you know that it really doesn't matter what dog the judge selects as the winner. Whether you win or not, this much is certain: The most wonderful dog in the world is—*your dog*.

index of dogs